HEINEMANN GEOGRAPHY for AVERY HILL

CW00590345

PROBLEM SOLVING PRACTICE

Heinemann

Paul Brooker • Geoff Brookes • Andy Leeder

Heinemann Educational Publishers
Halley Court, Jordan Hill, Oxford OX2 8EJ
Part of Harcourt Education

Heinemann is the registered trademark of Harcourt Education Limited

Text © Paul Brooker, Geoff Brookes and Andy Leeder, 2001

First published in 2001

ISBN 0 435 35405 1

05
10 9 8 7 6 5 4

Cover photographs of Mississippi, Illinois by Stone
Cover design by Paintbox Design
Original illustrations @ Heinemann Educational Publishers Ltd
Designed and typeset by The Wooden Ark, Leeds
Printed and bound in Spain by Edelvives

British Library Cataloguing in Publication Data
A catalogue record for this book is available from the British Library

Acknowledgements
The publishers would like to thank the following for permission to reproduce copyright material:

Maps and extracts:
p.6B R. Robinson, Brazil - Country Studies Series; p.6C Chambers and Currie, Climate, The Environment and People / Heinemann; p.9B Philips Modern School Atlas / George Philip Ltd; p.18A USA Today 23rd October 2000; p.18L The Seattle Post 28th June 2000; p.18R The Associated Press 25th September 1998; p.23C Shelley Behnken; p.23D, 26I The National Hurricane Centre; p.32/33 Philips University Atlas / George Philip Ltd; p.46A Maps reproduced from Ordnance Survey mapping with the permission of the Controller of Her Majesty's Stationery Office, © Crown copyright, License no. 10000230; p.52C Philips Modern School Atlas / George Philip Ltd; p.52D K. Taylor, Human Society and the Global Economy / 1996; p.56A Inter-American Development Bank 1996; p.66B Maps reproduced from Ordnance Survey mapping with the permission of the Controller of Her Majesty's Stationery Office, © Crown copyright, License no. 10000230; p.68A Phillip Woodhaus; p.68C, 69C Kettering Evening Telegraph 1st September 2000; p.72C David Waugh, The New Wider World / Thomas Nelson & Sons 1998; p.78B Korean Electronics Company; p.82B The Broads Authority; p.83D P Heath / Broadcaster 2000; p.84A Peninsula Cottages / Norwich and Norfolk Broads and Countryside; p.84B Waterside Terrace Restaurant and Bar / Eating Out in the Broads 2000; p.85A Broads Tours; Waveney River Centre; Sutton Windmill and Broads Museum; p.86E Karen Barker / Broads Environmental Education Authority; p.87I Norfolk School of Canoeing; p.87G, 88L The Broads Authority 1996; p.88M Fairhaven Woodland and Water Garden; p.89B Maps reproduced from Ordnance Survey mapping with the permission of the Controller of Her Majesty's Stationery Office, © Crown copyright, License no. 10000230.

Photographs:
p.5 South American Pictures/Tony Morrison; p.12(1) Sue Cunningham Photographic/Sue Cunningham; p.12(2) Sue Cunningham Photographic/Sue Cunningham; p.12(3) South American Pictures/Tony Morrison; p.12(4) South American Pictures/Tony Morrison; p.12 (bottom) Panos Pictures/Jerry Callow; p.17 Associated Press/Lou Krasky; p.18(1) Science Photo Library/NASA; p.18(2)KTP Power Photos; p.20(1) FLPA/US Army; p.20(2)Still Pictures/G. Wiltsie-Peter Arnold Inc.; p.20(3) Still Pictures/Laura Dwight; p.20(4) FLPA/Mark Newman; p.21(1) Mary Evans Picture Library/L'Illustrazione; p.21(2) Associated Press; p.21(3) Science Photo Library/NASA; p.21(4)Popperfoto; p.21(5) The Stock Market Photo Agency Inc.; p.22 Science Photo Library/NASA/Goddard Space Flight Centre; p.23 Associated Press/Chuck Burton; p.29 Corbis/James Davies/Eye Ubiquitous; p.32(1) Still Pictures/Malcolm Watson; p.33 Hutchinson Library/Robert Francis; p.35(top) Corbis/Keren Su; p.35(bottom)Associated Press, Xinhua; p.37 Still Pictures/Hartmut Schwarzbach; p.38 Corbis/Keren Su; p.41 Environmental Images/Jim Hodson; p.42 Eye Ubiquitous/Bobatt Casby; p.44(top) Aerofilms Ltd; p.44(bottom) Roger Scruton; p.45(top) Hull Daily Mail Publications; p.45(middle) Hull Daily Mail Publications; p.45(bottom) Hull Daily Mail Publications; p.46 Hull Daily Mail Publications; p.47(top) John T Blakeston; p.47 (bottom) Hull Daily Mail Publications; p.49 Roger Scruton; p.51 Panos Pictures/ Paul Smith; p.53 South American Pictures/Tony Morrison; p.54(top) South American Pictures/Tony Morrison; p.54(bottom) Panos Pictures/Jon Spaull; p.55(1) Panos Pictures/Sue Cunningham; p.55(2) South American Pictures/Tony Morrison; p.55(3)Panos Pictures/Sean Sprague; p.56(1) Panos Pictures/Paul Smith; p.56(2) Panos Pictures/Maria Luiza; p.56(3) Sue Cunningham Photographic/Sue Cunningham; p.59 South American Pictures/Robert Francis; p.61 Format Photographers/Paula Solloway; p.64 Eye Ubiquitous/Bob Battersby; p.70 Collections/Robert Deane; p.71 Science Photo Library/Richard T. Nowitz; p.74(1)Corbis; p.74(2)Corbis; p.74(3)Corbis; p.74(4)Corbis; p.81 Collections/John D. Beldom; p.83(top)Bruce Coleman Collection/Orion Press; p.83(bottom)Collections/David M Hughes; p.86(top)Robert Harding/P Craven; p.86(middle)Ecoscene/Nick Hawkes; p.86(bottom)Ecoscene/PT; p.87 Robert Harding; p.88 Collections/Gill Jones; p.89(left) Collections/John D Beldom; p.89(right) Collections/John D Beldom

The publishers have made every effort to contact copyright holders. However, if any material has been incorrectly acknowledged, the publishers would be pleased to correct this at the earliest opportunity

Tel: 01865 888058 www.heinemann.co.uk

Contents

Contents

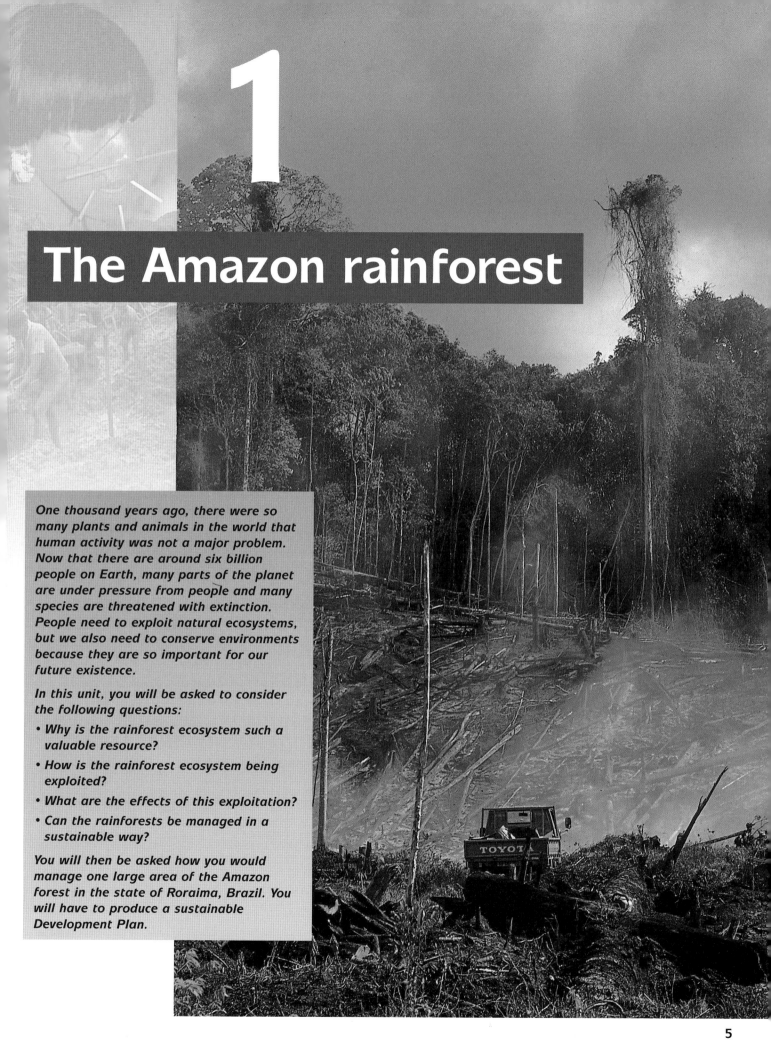

1

The Amazon rainforest

One thousand years ago, there were so many plants and animals in the world that human activity was not a major problem. Now that there are around six billion people on Earth, many parts of the planet are under pressure from people and many species are threatened with extinction. People need to exploit natural ecosystems, but we also need to conserve environments because they are so important for our future existence.

In this unit, you will be asked to consider the following questions:

• Why is the rainforest ecosystem such a valuable resource?

• How is the rainforest ecosystem being exploited?

• What are the effects of this exploitation?

• Can the rainforests be managed in a sustainable way?

You will then be asked how you would manage one large area of the Amazon forest in the state of Roraima, Brazil. You will have to produce a sustainable Development Plan.

Why is the rainforest so valuable?

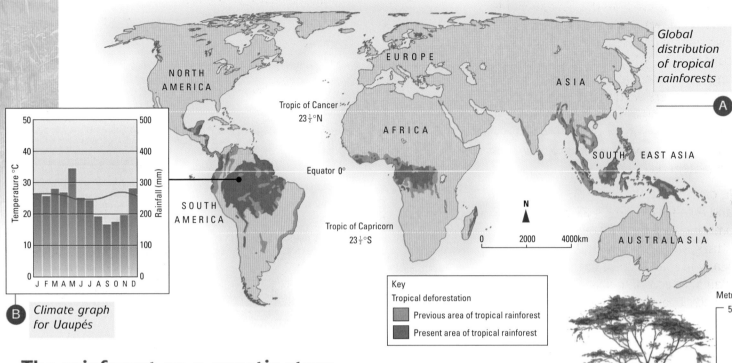

Global distribution of tropical rainforests

A

Key
Tropical deforestation

Previous area of tropical rainforest

Present area of tropical rainforest

B Climate graph for Uaupés

The rainforest as a genetic store

The tropical rainforests once covered 14 per cent of the Earth's land area. They are still the world's largest and most complex ecosystem. **Source A** shows the distribution of tropical rainforests, stretching along the Equator, between the Tropics of Cancer and Capricorn. Although clearance has reduced rainforests to less than six per cent of the Earth's land area, the rainforest ecosystem still contains an estimated 50 per cent of all the world's plant and animal species. These forests are the Earth's greatest store of ecological **biodiversity**. There are approximately 1.4 million named species on Earth, but scientists estimate that there might be as many as 80 million different organisms on the planet, of which 60 per cent are insects.

Producers (plants) need water, warmth, sunlight and a good supply of nutrients to grow well. **Source B** shows that the equatorial climate is ideal for vegetation growth all year round. Almost anything can grow in these hot and humid conditions, but with so many plants fighting for space, there are two things in short supply – light and nutrients:

Not every plant can be as tall as the trees in the **canopy**, so other species have had to adapt to get the light and nutrients they need to survive. The rainforest ecosystem has had 90 million years to adapt, so thousands of different plant species have found a niche in the ecosystem. **Source C** shows some of the ways that the trees and other plants have adapted to the climate and environment.

Light – all plants try to get as much as possible. The most successful plants are therefore tall and have big leaves. These tall trees shade the other vegetation.

The tropical rainforest ecosystem

C

Nutrients stores:
80% in vegetation
20% in soil

Nutrients – all plants need a food supply. The most successful plants extract their nutrients from the soil as quickly as possible through their roots. The soil is therefore poor, as it cannot store many nutrients.

Q
1 What are the components of the rainforest ecosystem?
2 Why do rainforest ecosystems have such a diversity of species?

The rich vegetation is a perfect food source for consumer species. Therefore more herbivore species (**primary consumers**) live here than in any other ecosystem, which means that there are also more carnivores (**secondary consumers**). With all these living organisms, there are thousands of **decomposers** waiting to recycle the dead vegetation and other organic matter. With so many different species, the rainforest has the most complex **food webs** of any ecosystem on Earth.

In order to survive, many plants, insects and animals have evolved the most amazing variety of defences against attack, with clever camouflage or poisons. Many of the chemical compounds that plants, insects and animals produce have already been used by people in the rainforests and elsewhere. **Source D** shows just some of the rainforest species that people have exploited.

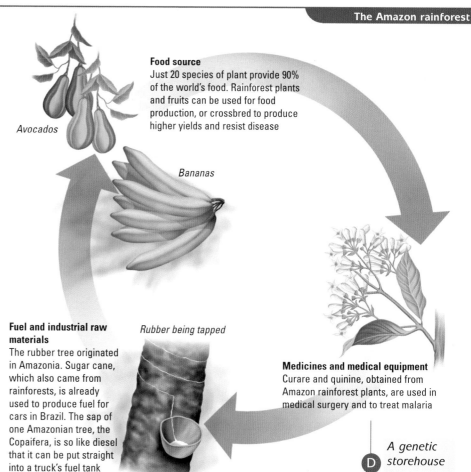

Food source
Just 20 species of plant provide 90% of the world's food. Rainforest plants and fruits can be used for food production, or crossbred to produce higher yields and resist disease

Avocados

Bananas

Fuel and industrial raw materials
The rubber tree originated in Amazonia. Sugar cane, which also came from rainforests, is already used to produce fuel for cars in Brazil. The sap of one Amazonian tree, the Copaifera, is so like diesel that it can be put straight into a truck's fuel tank

Rubber being tapped

Medicines and medical equipment
Curare and quinine, obtained from Amazon rainforest plants, are used in medical surgery and to treat malaria

D *A genetic storehouse*

The rainforest as a climate control

Within 48 hours of rain falling, 75% of it has been evaporated or transpired by plants to form clouds and further rain. This process is repeated as many as seven times before the rain clouds reach the Andes.

Rainforest is the result of the climate, but the forest also influences the weather and climate. **Source E** shows how vapour comes from the canopy. The daily heating of the forest causes **transpiration** out of leaves and **evaporation** from surface water. This water rises as vapour, before cooling, condensing and falling again as rain. On average, rainforests have 75–100 of these convectional thunderstorms every year. Without the forest to store the rainwater, it would simply run off into rivers and be lost from the ecosystem. Rainforests keep the climate wet. Trees also fulfil a vital function in absorbing carbon dioxide (CO_2) from the atmosphere and respiring oxygen. Plants take in the CO_2 and give out O_2 and keep the atmospheric gases in balance. Too much CO_2 could, in future, cause serious global climatic problems.

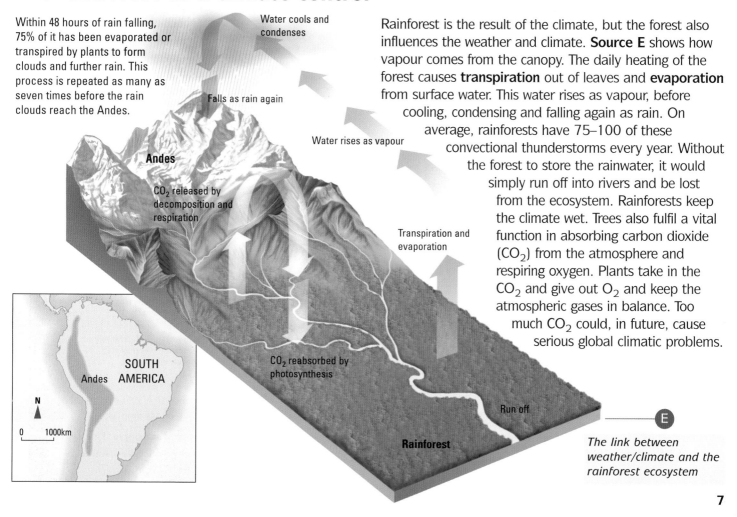

Water cools and condenses

Falls as rain again

Water rises as vapour

Andes

CO_2 released by decomposition and respiration

Transpiration and evaporation

SOUTH AMERICA

Andes

N

0   1000km

CO_2 reabsorbed by photosynthesis

Run off

Rainforest

E *The link between weather/climate and the rainforest ecosystem*

Who exploits the tropical rainforest?

Traditional exploitation by the Yanomami

Indigenous people, like the Yanomami tribe, have lived in rainforests for thousands of years. In 1900 there were 1 million 'Indians' living in Brazil, but today there are less than 200 000. In Roraima, a region of Amazonia, 9 000 Yanomami live in an area of 10 000 square kilometres of rainforest. These indigenous people have always exploited the ecosystem to get everything they need to survive. Traditionally, the Yanomami get their food by:

- hunting animals
- gathering fruit and other forest foods
- growing crops in 'shifting cultivation plots'.

Source A shows how their farms work, so that the water cycle, the soil nutrients and ecosystem are kept in balance and not destroyed.

When the Yanomami collect food and hunt animals, they are always careful not to over-exploit the local resources, because they know that they must have enough food in future. If food resources become difficult to find and hunters have to travel too far, then the Yanomami will move to a different location and set up a new village within their territory. They do not harm the environment, so their way of life is sustainable.

Yanomami use axes and fires to clear a small area of forest

Shifting cultivation in Amazonia – Yanomami Indians

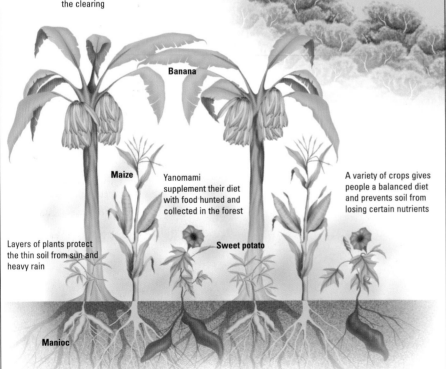

Valuable trees are left. These provide shade and food products e.g. fruit, brazil nuts or rubber

Yanomami plant a mixture of food crops, scattered over the clearing

Banana

Maize

Yanomami supplement their diet with food hunted and collected in the forest

A variety of crops gives people a balanced diet and prevents soil from losing certain nutrients

Sweet potato

Layers of plants protect the thin soil from sun and heavy rain

Manioc

After 3 or 4 years
- soils lose some fertility
- animal and insect pests attack crops
- weeds invade the site
so the Yanomami abandon the field and clear another area

After 20 years, this clearing will grow back and the forest soils will recover their fertility

> **Q** Explain how the Yanomami way of life is sustainable. Refer to:
> - plants and wildlife
> - the soil and its nutrients
> - the water cycle.

Modern exploitation in Amazonia

Europeans first colonised the coastal areas of Brazil in 1500. The country's population now exceeds 160 million, but modern exploitation of Amazonia did not develop until the trans-Amazon network of roads was started in the 1970s. Brazil is a NIC (newly industrialising country) and wants to exploit the rainforest areas because:

- most people live near the coast in the SE of Brazil. Other regions of Brazil, such as the NE, are over populated. Amazonia is sparsely populated. There is plenty of space for the development of new settlements in the rainforest.

- Brazil is developing its economy at a rapid rate. It needs to develop its natural resources for economic development – trade exports, agricultural and industrial development. It can also raise living standards for the Brazilian people (see **Source C**).

Brazil has one-third of the world's rainforest, but in recent years 12 per cent of Brazil's forest has been cleared. **Source B** shows the pattern of the destruction in Amazonia.

	Brazil	UK
Population	160 million	58 million
Population growth rate	1.8 per cent per year	0.1 per cent per year
Life expectancy	62 years	76 years
GNP per person (US$)	$ 2900	$ 18000
Infant mortality (children 0–1)	57 per 1000	8 per 1000

Socio-economic data on Brazil and the UK

Q

1 Describe the location of rainforests in Brazil.

2 Describe the pattern of rainforest clearance and suggest two reasons for the distribution of clearance.

B Rainforest destruction in Brazil

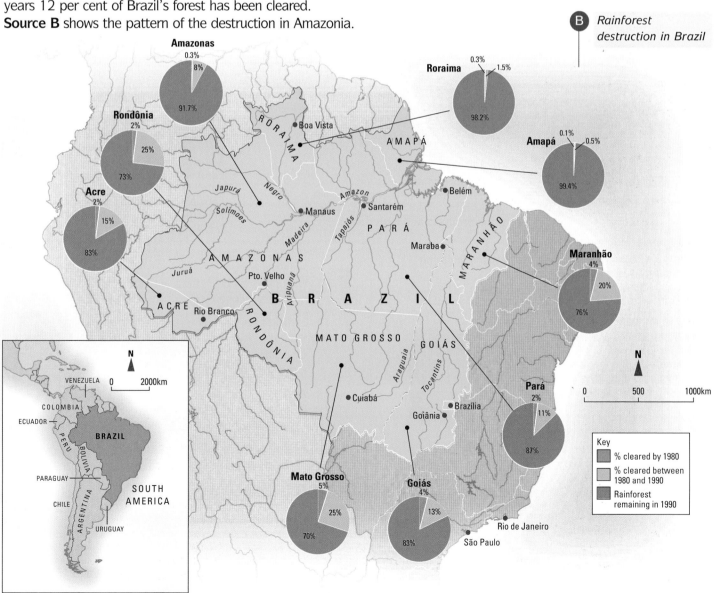

How does economic activity exploit the rainforest?

Cattle ranching
- Over 25% of the forest cleared is used for large-scale cattle ranching.
- Forest is cut down and burned.
- Grasses grow on the cleared land.
- Cattle are reared for the mass production of cheap beef.

Harvesting and rubber extraction
- Smallholders gather Brazil nuts, spices and forest fruits.
- Rubber is 'tapped' from wild trees.
- Products are sold to local markets.

Logging
- Thousands of loggers cut down trees for timber.
- Valuable hardwoods such as mahogany and teak are sold for export, bringing Brazil millions of dollars.
- Other timber is pulped for paper production.

Tourism
- Tourists travel from all over the world to see Amazonia's unique plants and wildlife.

Scientific research
- Scientists gather plants for research, and chemical compounds are used to make medicines, new food products and materials.

Resettlement
- Resettlement of people from other over-populated parts of Brazil
- Poor farmers are encouraged to settle in Amazonia.
- Land is cleared for thousands of small farms.
- Farmers grow food for their families and move on to new plots when soil fertility declines.

Industrial developments
- Many raw materials are used by the manufacturing industry: boat building, food processing.
- Wood is used for charcoal in industrial furnaces.

Trade in animals
- Millions of live animals are sold to dealers.
- Animals such as jaguars, snakes and alligators are hunted for furs and skins.
- An estimated 12 million animals are smuggled out of Amazonia each year giving dealers $1.5 billion.

Plantations
- Rubber, teak, cocoa, pineapple and other trees are planted to make harvesting more efficient. Plantations are vulnerable to disease and parasites.

Q
1 How does each of these activities exploit the rainforest ecosystem?

2 Explain how each of the following is used:
 - plants
 - wildlife
 - the soil and its nutrients.

3 Which activities:
 - destroy the forest ecosystem?
 - need to conserve the forest ecosystem?

4 Use this scoring system to rank the activities in order of which ones most disrupt the ecosystem.

 5 = complete clearance over a wide area
 4 = widespread destruction of habitats
 3 = patchy clearance, but trees will recover
 2 = small-scale or localised disturbance or destruction
 1 = ecosystem processes slightly disturbed
 0 = no destruction or disturbance

How does modern exploitation affect the rainforest?

Clearing rainforest destroys the rainforest ecosystem because it breaks the different links that hold the ecosystem together. **Source A** shows the links in the chain. Because the rainforest is a system, one change has a 'knock on' effect to another component in the system. This can become a vicious circle.

Clearing forests affects people and also the weather, climate and hydrology of other parts of Brazil. Rainforests situated inland rely on water that has

already been through the forest water cycle. Clearing rainforest breaks this cycle and the rainwater returns to the ocean along rivers.

Many people claim that intense rainforest clearance is a prime cause of global warming, which will increase temperatures and raise sea levels. It will also alter the Earth's wind circulation, making some regions wetter and others drier.

A *Links in the rainforest ecosystem – what happens when trees are cut down*

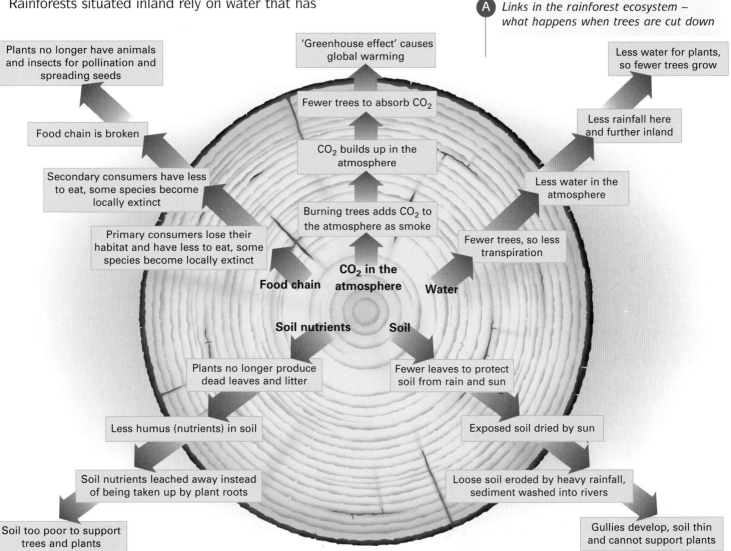

- Plants no longer have animals and insects for pollination and spreading seeds
- Food chain is broken
- Secondary consumers have less to eat, some species become locally extinct
- Primary consumers lose their habitat and have less to eat, some species become locally extinct
- 'Greenhouse effect' causes global warming
- Fewer trees to absorb CO_2
- CO_2 builds up in the atmosphere
- Burning trees adds CO_2 to the atmosphere as smoke
- **Food chain**
- **CO_2 in the atmosphere**
- **Water**
- Less water for plants, so fewer trees grow
- Less rainfall here and further inland
- Less water in the atmosphere
- Fewer trees, so less transpiration
- **Soil nutrients**
- **Soil**
- Plants no longer produce dead leaves and litter
- Fewer leaves to protect soil from rain and sun
- Less humus (nutrients) in soil
- Exposed soil dried by sun
- Soil nutrients leached away instead of being taken up by plant roots
- Loose soil eroded by heavy rainfall, sediment washed into rivers
- Soil too poor to support trees and plants
- Gullies develop, soil thin and cannot support plants

Q 1 How does rainforest clearance affect the ecosystem? Refer to these aspects of the ecosystem:
   - structure (the species in the ecosystem)
   - processes (nutrient cycling and food chains).

2 The Amazon rainforest is 90 million years old. Recent human activity has changed it. Does this mean that the ecosystem is stable or unstable?

3 How can human activity affect weather and climate?
   How does rainforest destruction affect global climate? Explain:
   - global warming
   - the greenhouse effect.

4 Is it fair to blame rainforest destruction for the greenhouse effect?

How does modern exploitation affect local people?

Opening up Amazonia for farming and logging has led to other developments that have economic and social impacts.

 A *The multiplier effect*

Gold
Gold is found in the river deposits over much of Amazonia. Large Multi-National Corporations (MNCs) exploit the resources, but much of the prospecting is undertaken by small groups of individual miners (garimpeiros) who seek their fortune in the forests. They use mercury to find the gold.

HEP
Amazon rivers have massive potential for the development of hydroelectric power. The Tucurui dam in Para is the fourth largest in the world. The lake flooded an area of rainforest five times the size of the Isle of Wight and displaced many indigenous Indians. The power provides electricity for local towns and for industry and factories on the coast, such as the huge aluminium plant at São Luis.

Mining
Amazonia has some of the world's richest mineral resources. The Carajas project has developed the world's biggest iron ore deposits, as well as gold, silver, manganese and bauxite.

Roads and settlements
Along with mining and hydroelectric power developments come roads and settlements. All these new land uses destroy rainforest.

Economic benefits and social costs

The economic impact is often good for Brazilians, so there are also social benefits, such as improved living standards and a better quality of life. People as far away as São Paulo can get employment in steel works and car factories that use the iron ore from Amazonia. Electricity from the hydroelectric plant (HEP) stations makes life easier for millions of people, but what about the **social costs**? People who live in Amazonia have faced conflict and problems from miners, ranchers, loggers and other developers. **Source B** outlines some of these problems.

Indigenous Indian groups
The people most affected are the indigenous Indians, like the Yanomami, who have lived in the rainforest for thousands of years. There is conflict between the Indians and the new colonisers.

- If land is cleared, the Yanomami lose the resources that they need to survive.
- They have to compete with newcomers for food.
- The Yanomami have no immunity to diseases such as 'flu' and measles, and consequently die if these diseases are passed on.
- The river water is polluted with mercury and cadmium from gold prospecting. Mercury and cadmium cause deformity in unborn babies and death.

Q What are the economic benefits of rainforest developments?

 B *Indigenous Indian groups*

What is sustainability?

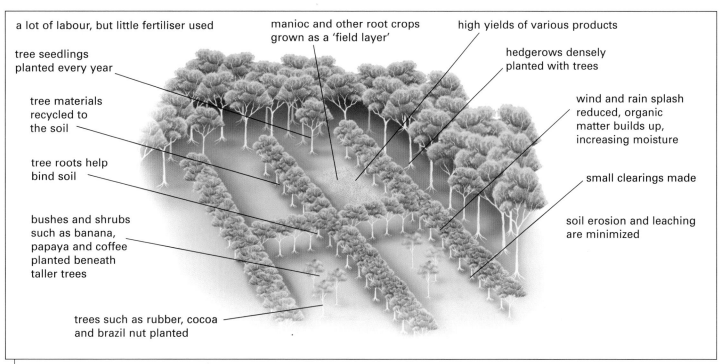

a lot of labour, but little fertiliser used

tree seedlings planted every year

tree materials recycled to the soil

tree roots help bind soil

bushes and shrubs such as banana, papaya and coffee planted beneath taller trees

trees such as rubber, cocoa and brazil nut planted

manioc and other root crops grown as a 'field layer'

high yields of various products

hedgerows densely planted with trees

wind and rain splash reduced, organic matter builds up, increasing moisture

small clearings made

soil erosion and leaching are minimized

 A   *Agroforestry farm with hedgerows*

Sustainable developments can be carried on for many years because they do not harm people or the environment. They are carefully planned and managed. Resources are renewed so that future generations can continue the activities.

 B   *Sustainable developments*

Sustainable farming or **agroforestry** is like a 'shifting cultivation' plot. Farmers plant crops and trees together so soil is protected from the tropical weather. **Source A** shows how it works.

There are two types of sustainable wildlife areas. An **ecological reserve** is an area rich in wildlife that is completely protected from exploitation and development. The Xixuau-Xiparina (X-X) area of Roraima is 1700 km². Less than 1000 people live here and it is a habitat for many rare wildlife species, including:

- giant otter
- jaguar
- giant anteater
- river dolphins
- black caymen (alligator)
- harpy eagle.

An **extractive reserve** belongs to the state. No trees are felled or damaged, but local people have limited farming and fishing rights and can collect forest products. Forest products include:

- rubber
- brazil nuts
- fruits
- lianas (for natural fibres)
- specimen plants for scientific research.

This is sustainable because plants can regenerate naturally and the rainforest is unharmed. It is an ideal place for scientific research into rainforest species.

Q   Do some research on the Internet. Use key words such as 'Tucurui', 'Carajas', 'Chico Mendes', 'ecotours' or 'Worldwide Fund for Nature'.
Are tour operators really offering 'ecotourism' by following the rules set out below?

In the forestry industry there is so much rainforest that most loggers 'clear fell' whole areas of woodland to find the most valuable trees. One cubic metre of mahogany is worth over $850, and a 40m tree is so valuable that it is worth making a special road, even if the tree is 500km away from the sawmill. Replanting trees is not worthwhile for loggers, since trees take more than 100 years to mature. This is known as **unsustainable forestry.**

With **sustainable forestry,** either one tree is replanted for each tree felled or the logging is undertaken in thin lines through the rainforest. The clearings let in light and the rainforest regenerates naturally, without the problems of soil erosion from large clearings.

Some travel companies advertise **'ecotourism'** holidays just because they offer a look at a few animals, in the wild, but ecotourism is more than this. It is a special kind of holiday package that helps people in rural communities to improve their lives, while conserving the natural environment that they depend on. To do this, ecotourism must:

- be small scale, with small numbers of tourists
- be controlled by local people
- educate tourists
- not pollute or pressurise the local environment and wildlife
- put money into local communities and the environment.

How should the rainforest ecosystem be managed?

Two opposing plans have been put forward for Roraima. The details are given below.

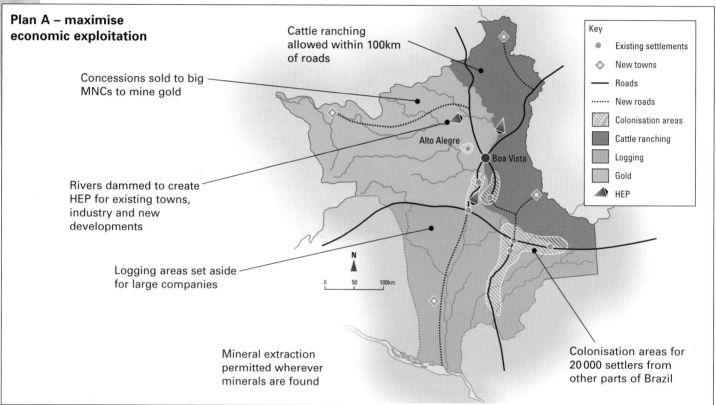

Plan A – maximise economic exploitation

Cattle ranching allowed within 100km of roads

Concessions sold to big MNCs to mine gold

Rivers dammed to create HEP for existing towns, industry and new developments

Logging areas set aside for large companies

Mineral extraction permitted wherever minerals are found

Colonisation areas for 20 000 settlers from other parts of Brazil

Key

- ● Existing settlements
- ◇ New towns
- —— Roads
- ······ New roads
- ▨ Colonisation areas
- ▩ Cattle ranching
- ▦ Logging
- ▧ Gold
- ◣ HEP

Alto Alegre
Boa Vista

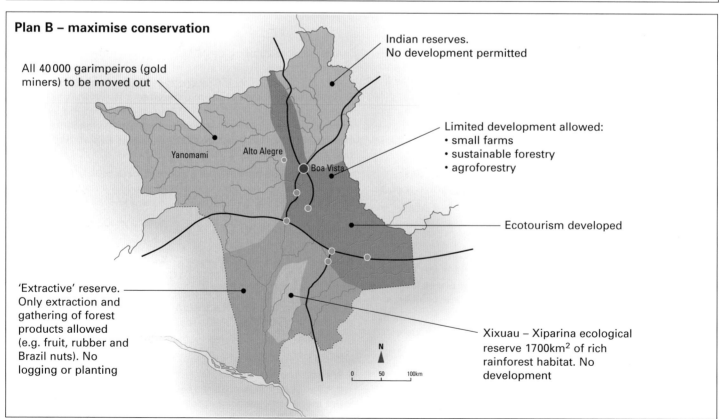

Plan B – maximise conservation

All 40 000 garimpeiros (gold miners) to be moved out

Indian reserves. No development permitted

Limited development allowed:
- small farms
- sustainable forestry
- agroforestry

Ecotourism developed

'Extractive' reserve. Only extraction and gathering of forest products allowed (e.g. fruit, rubber and Brazil nuts). No logging or planting

Xixuau – Xiparina ecological reserve 1700km² of rich rainforest habitat. No development

Yanomami
Alto Alegre
Boa Vista

Roraima today

Population (thousands)					
1950	1960	1970	1980	1990	2000
19	25	43	75	275	350

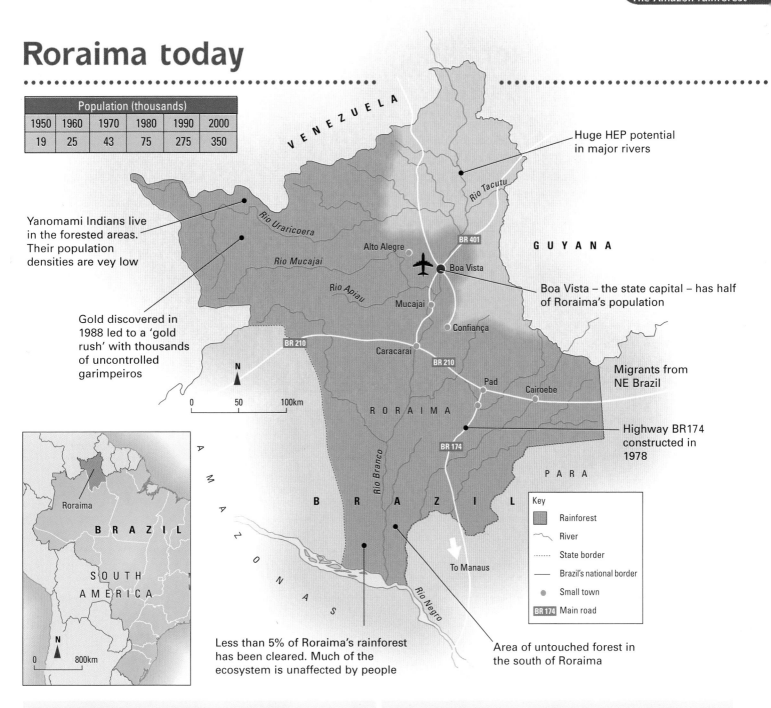

Huge HEP potential in major rivers

Yanomami Indians live in the forested areas. Their population densities are vey low

Gold discovered in 1988 led to a 'gold rush' with thousands of uncontrolled garimpeiros

Boa Vista – the state capital – has half of Roraima's population

Migrants from NE Brazil

Highway BR174 constructed in 1978

Less than 5% of Roraima's rainforest has been cleared. Much of the ecosystem is unaffected by people

Area of untouched forest in the south of Roraima

Key
- Rainforest
- River
- State border
- Brazil's national border
- Small town
- BR 174 Main road

Your decision

You have been asked to produce a Development Plan for the State of Roraima. The plan should aim to exploit and conserve the resources of Roraima's rainforest. You can keep or adapt the two plans on page 14.
You should consider the following:

1 What are the benefits for:
   a local indigenous people
   b other local people
   c the people of Brazil?

2 How will the environment be conserved?
   a local ecosystems
   b local water, weather and climate
   c global climate

3 How can your plan be sustained in the long term?

Your task

Draw an annotated sketch map to show your development plan. Design it in a similar way to the plans on page 14.
Write a three-minute speech that justifies your ideas. In your justification you must explain:

- the main priority of your development plan.
- why you chose to allow certain land uses and not others.
- the size and location of each of your chosen developments.
- how and why your plan will exploit the rainforest.
- how and why your plan will conserve the rainforest.

Review exercise

1 Look at the mind map below. It summarises some of the issues about exploitation of the Amazon rainforest ecosystem. Use it to complete a mind map of your own, with illustrations.

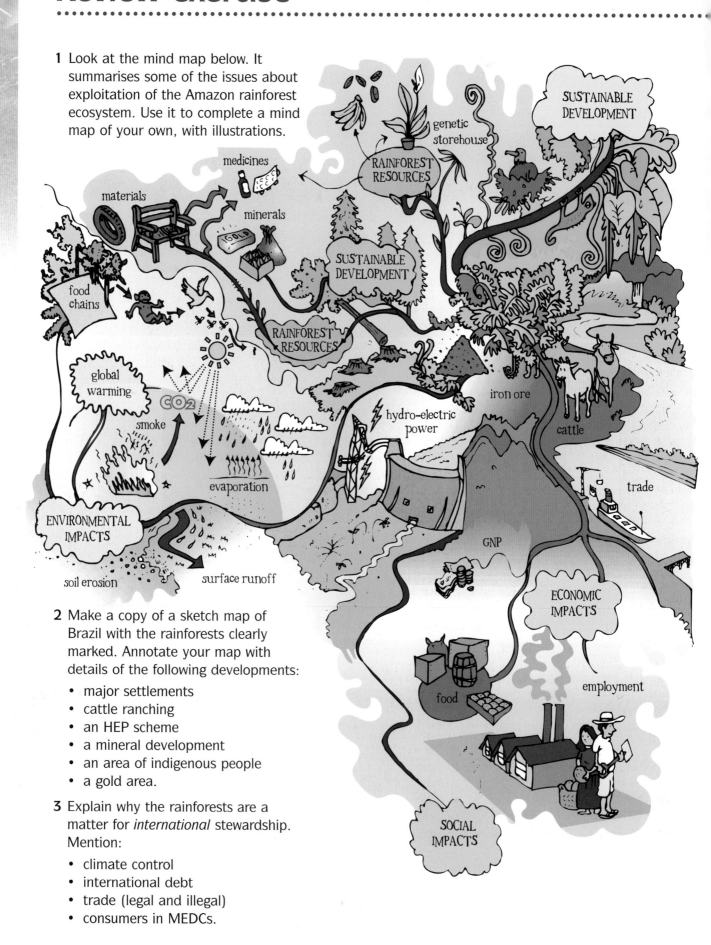

2 Make a copy of a sketch map of Brazil with the rainforests clearly marked. Annotate your map with details of the following developments:

- major settlements
- cattle ranching
- an HEP scheme
- a mineral development
- an area of indigenous people
- a gold area.

3 Explain why the rainforests are a matter for *international* stewardship. Mention:

- climate control
- international debt
- trade (legal and illegal)
- consumers in MEDCs.

Extreme weather events

Extreme weather events make great news. The stories can dominate the news broadcasts for many days, with dramatic pictures of the event itself and the chaos it leaves behind. Sadly, we can all see the great suffering such events bring and the enormous challenges people face as they attempt to recover.

*Problem solving in this case is not about prevention. Even the most powerful country on earth cannot control what nature chooses to throw at it. The Unites States experiences more than its fair share of **hurricanes**, **floods**, **droughts** and **blizzards**. On each occasion, the impact on people and the community in which they live is enormous.*

This unit looks at the way people respond to such events, the choices they make and how difficult it is to reach decisions. In this unit you will be asked to consider the following:

- *What extreme events affected the US in the twentieth century?*

- *What are the consequences of such events?*

- *How can the people affected respond?*

- *Why do hurricanes present particularly difficult challenges for those in authority?*

You will then be asked to consider a strategy for coping with the threat of a hurricane. The case study is Lee County, Florida. The area has a long history of dealing with the hurricane threat and scientists predict that the threat is even greater over the next 25 years. Whatever strategies you consider, you will be asked to justify your plans and recognise that your decisions may not please all of the people, all of the time.

Violent weather – spectacular and deadly!

Weather events can be dramatic. Spectacular to witness, often frightening to experience, they can lead to deaths and huge financial losses. They have never touched most of us – hurricanes, blizzards, heat waves and floods are things that you read about in newspapers or see on the television. The US experiences many such events. Modern communications ensure that we are all kept informed of the misery that people face, even though they are thousands of kilometres away.

Occasionally, weather events can be just irritating or inconvenient. **Source A** gives three examples of how the weather can have an impact on peoples lives, without causing pain and misery.

> **Q**
> 1 Find your own examples of extreme weather events that can be said to be inconvenient. Can they sometimes create opportunities for people?
>
> 2 Why do extreme events in LEDCs often cause greater loss of life and financial hardship? Find examples and discuss this with your teacher.

 Inconvenient weather events!

US Shuttle Discovery delayed by strong winds

Strong winds in Florida and rain clouds in California have prevented the US Shuttle Discovery from returning to Earth on Monday. It was the second day in a row that bad weather kept the shuttle from landing, dragging the flight out to 13 days.

Mission control explained that the preferred landing site is the Kennedy Space Centre in Florida. 'If we land the Shuttle at the Edwards Air Force Base in California, it costs us nearly $1 million to transport the Shuttle across the country. The week-long journey could delay the Discovery's next mission, which is scheduled for next February.'

Of the 98 previous Shuttle landings, only 52 have ended up at Kennedy. It seems that poor weather in Florida, famous for its sunshine, is not only inconvenient, it's expensive.

Source: adapted from USA Today, 23 October 2000

Phew!

John Grosso is the owner of 'Allied Ice', which supplies ice to hotels and restaurants in the Seattle area. He doesn't expect any of his workers to take their holidays between May and October. 'It's our busy period,' he explained. 'The ice business is seasonal, you need to produce it when people want it.'

Running any business dependent on the weather is always problematic. The heat wave that hit the north-west coast in June 2000 gave John Grosso particular problems.

'When it's hot out here, demand for ice is almost instant. In the last month, production has been 24 hours a day. Our trucks are rolling from 7.00 am to 10.00 pm,' he explained.

Some like it hot, and if you're in the ice-making business, the hotter the better!

George cancels showdown

The approach of Hurricane George led Miami to cancel the scheduled football game against rivals UCLA.

Miami president, Tad Foote, explained that the safety of fans and players was the main consideration. Warnings of 105 mph winds were enough to convince all those involved that the decision was the right one.

Nevertheless, the cancellation will have serious consequences. CBS had planned to show the game live on national TV. They will now have the problem of plugging the broadcast gap and compensating the advertisers. Support services had already prepared 80 000 meals!

Source: adapted from the Seattle Post, 28 June 2000

Source: adapted from a posting in the Associated Press, 25 September 1998

Source B illustrates how, all too often, violent weather can lead to tragedy. It also shows just why the US Government is determined to reduce the impact of severe weather. In the period 1980–2000, the US experienced 40 weather-related disasters, each causing damage of more than $1 billion. Total costs exceeded $200 billion. These figures hide the real tragedy of over 15000 deaths. If the problem itself cannot be tackled, there is an obvious incentive to reduce the impact of such events.

1 **Hurricane Floyd (Sept 99)**
High winds, severe flooding along eastern coast.
$6.0 billion damages; 77 deaths

2 **Southern Heat Wave + Drought (summer 98)**
Across southern states. Serious damage to agriculture and ranching.
$7.5 billion damages; 200 deaths

3 **Lower Mississippi catchment (May 95)**
Floods associated with torrential rainfall and tornadoes
$6.1 billion damages; 32 deaths

4 **Storm of the Century (March 93)**
Hits eastern coast. High winds with heavy snow.
$5.0 billion damages; 270 deaths

5 **Hurricane Andrew (August 92)**
High winds destroy 125000 homes in Florida and Louisiana.
$32.4 billion damages; 61 deaths

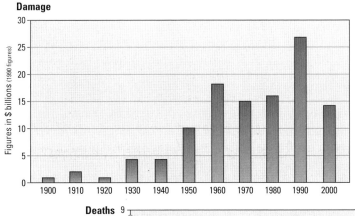

B Billion-dollar weather disasters

Legend:
- Hurricane
- Flood
- Lightening/Hail storm
- Blizzard
- Fire following drought + high winds
- Ice storm
- Heat wave/drought
- Frost (affects fruit growers)

1983 | $3.6
Date — Cost in billions

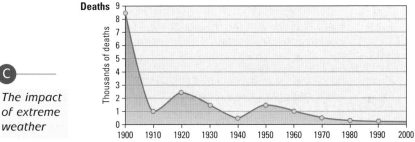

C The impact of extreme weather

Damage (Figures in $ billions (1990 figures))

Deaths (Thousands of deaths)

Problem solving?

The focus in this book is on problem solving! With regard to extreme weather events, people have little or no control over the event itself. We do not have the capability or the technology to solve, or even reduce, the root cause of the problem – our unstable atmosphere. In this case, problem solving is limited to dealing with the results of the catastrophe. How can loss of life be minimised? How can financial losses be reduced?

Q
1 Find out if there are any examples where people can control weather events.

2 Look at the graphs in **Source C**. What do they suggest about the ability of the US government to cope with extremes of weather?

Cause and effect of extreme weather

The victims of extreme weather are not really interested in the cause of the event, they want to know why they were the unlucky ones and what the local authorities and the national government are going to do to compensate them. The meteorological reasons behind such events are complex. The charts like those shown in **Source A** can signal the approach of problematic weather.

B **Different kinds of extreme weather**

Depending on the time of year, the location and the intensity of each **depression**, these weather systems can bring:
• blizzards
• hurricanes
• downpours.

A **Simplified synoptic charts suggesting the possibility of extreme weather**

March 1993 – storm of the century hits the northeast states

Depending on the time of year, the location and the intensity of each **anticyclone**, these weather systems can bring:
• heat waves
• droughts
• fog
• frost.

Summer 1998 – a southern heatwave

Q
1 Is there a link between financial loss and the number of deaths in the events described in Source C?

2 Which parts of the US are most vulnerable to a variety of extreme weather events?

Activity

Research one of these extreme weather events. Use the Internet. A good starting point is the US government site.

Use any good geography textbook to find out the cause of such extreme events. The *location* and *intensity* of anticyclones (high pressure systems) and depressions (low pressure systems) are important factors. The *time of the year* they occur is also significant.

When it comes to extremes of weather, solving the cause of the problem is not an option. Not even the most technologically advanced country in the world has the capability of preventing the event from happening.

In recent years, weather forecasting has become more sophisticated, enabling people to get advanced warnings of danger. Modern communications pass the news on in an instant. Both these developments are relatively new. **Source C** gives details of five events that have taken place in the last 80 years. A description of each event is given. Look at the way organisations reacted to the event. Problem solving is about looking ahead. How can we learn lessons from the past?

Extreme weather events

1927 – The Great Mississippi Flood

Above average rainfall across the entire river basin, combined with snow melt resulting from a sudden thaw in April, caused a rapid rise of the Mississippi.

Impact

Some 600 000 people forced from homes, 246 killed. Thousands of farm animals drown.

Response

The US government passes a Flood Control Act in 1928. Levees built along the Mississippi. Each State required to set up an emergency evacuation plan.

1930s – Heat wave and Drought in the Mid west

After record temperatures and low rainfall, high winds blow a 'black blizzard' of dust across Kansas, Texas and North and South Dakota

Impact

There is a huge increase in dust-related respiratory disease. Some 850 million tons of top soil is lost, devastating farms and farming communities. There is a mass movement of people away from the area to California.

Response

The US government plans a revolution in agriculture. Farmers are compelled to adopt new techniques such as crop rotation and contour ploughing.

1954/5 – The East Coast Hurricanes

A series of hurricanes take an unusual track. They move up the East Coast and cross the coast to hit New York, Connecticut and Massachusetts. High winds and associated storm tides hit parts of the US normally spared the worst of the annual hurricane season.

Impact

The hurricanes combine to cause 400 deaths and over $2 billion worth of damage. A significant proportion of the population is not insured against hurricane damage.

Response

The US government quadruples funds allocated to the National Oceanic and Atmospheric Administration and the National Hurricane Centre with a view to improving hurricane forecasting. Fifteen states increase the tax burden to build up their emergency funds.

1977 – The Great Freeze

Record low temperatures across eastern US. The Great Lakes freeze shore to shore, the sea freezes south to Chesapeake Bay. Blizzards follow, 30cm of snow falls in 24 hours, drifting to 8m snowdrifts in Buffalo, New York.

Impact

Some 3000 motorists stranded on route 128 for 48 hours. There are 29 deaths. Power lines snap under the weight of ice. Millions without electricity in the populated NE.

Response

Nine states combine to develop an early warning system for weather extremes and produce an education programme warning about the danger of hypothermia. Rhode Island invests in 500 snow ploughs.

1995 – Mid west Hit by Prolonged Heatwave

Temperatures exceed 106°F, but this is combined with high humidity. Minimum night-time temperatures do not go below 80°F. The event is rare. City authorities have no action plan.

Impact

Some 1000 deaths in total (465 in Chicago). Absenteeism from work increases tenfold. Schools close, hospitals for emergencies only.

Response

Chicago sets up emergency air-conditioned shelters. Heat waves are added to the list of recognised national disasters. This allows emergency state funds to be released.

Case study: the impact of Hurricane Floyd

The population of the eastern seaboard of the US receives regular reminders of the need to plan for catastrophic events. Hurricanes are a fact of life for many between the months of August and October. Hurricane Floyd hit in September 1999.

What are hurricanes?

Hurricanes are intense low pressure systems. They form in the tropics, where their energy is gained from the heat and moisture that are found in tropical seas. A column of air rises rapidly above the sea. Air near the surface rushes into the space created but spirals due to the rotation of the Earth.

Was Hurricane Floyd special?

Hurricane Floyd may not have had the strongest winds ever found in a hurricane (Typically, they reached 90 knots), but the sheer size of the spiral exceeded anything previously recorded. Hurricane Floyd also set records for the amount of rain it released onto the East Coast. It was remarkable for how long it lasted. **Source A** shows how Hurricane Floyd moved up the coast. **Source B** shows the eye of a hurricane and outlines the damage involved.

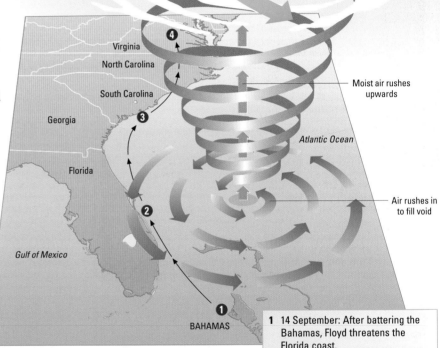

A The track of Hurricane Floyd

Moist air rushes upwards

Atlantic Ocean

Air rushes in to fill void

B The impact of Hurricane Floyd

1 **14 September:** After battering the Bahamas, Floyd threatens the Florida coast.

2 **14/15 September:** After a state of emergency is declared in Florida, Floyd turns north.

3 **15 September:** Floyd reaches the mainland to devastate the Carolinas.

4 **16/18 September:** Floyd continues north causing destruction in eight states.

Q

1 Find out how hurricanes are categorised.

2 Why is the hurricane season, in this area, limited to the period of August to October?

An eyewitness account

Eyewitness accounts give dramatic details of the impact of hurricanes.

Shelley Behnken, a resident of North Carolina, posted a diary on the Internet. Extracts from her diary are given in **Source C**.

C *Diary extract 15–20 September 1999*

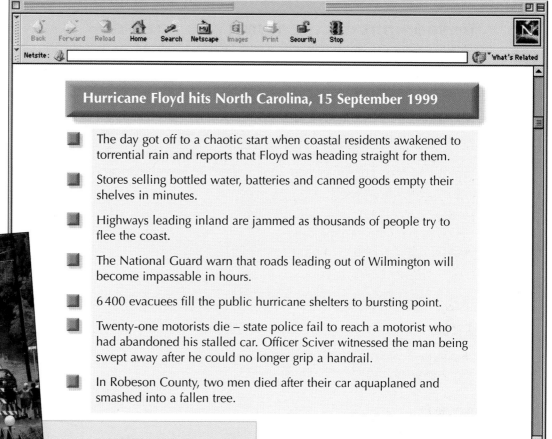

Hurricane Floyd hits North Carolina, 15 September 1999

- The day got off to a chaotic start when coastal residents awakened to torrential rain and reports that Floyd was heading straight for them.

- Stores selling bottled water, batteries and canned goods empty their shelves in minutes.

- Highways leading inland are jammed as thousands of people try to flee the coast.

- The National Guard warn that roads leading out of Wilmington will become impassable in hours.

- 6 400 evacuees fill the public hurricane shelters to bursting point.

- Twenty-one motorists die – state police fail to reach a motorist who had abandoned his stalled car. Officer Sciver witnessed the man being swept away after he could no longer grip a handrail.

- In Robeson County, two men died after their car aquaplaned and smashed into a fallen tree.

Our research suggests that the Atlantic Basin will see many decades of increased hurricane activity. Some of the hurricanes will be particularly intense.

All the signals for this are clear – higher than average temperatures in the North Atlantic Ocean and greater salt concentrations in the water, both of these were recorded before previous active hurricane periods.

William Gray, Professor of Atmospheric Science at Colorado State University

Global weather patterns are changing due to the impact of El Niño. Higher sea temperatures in the Pacific Ocean have an impact on global weather patterns, particularly the path and strength of trade winds. Years of research will be required to understand these changes. What we do know is that trade winds help to feed developing hurricanes, they bring the food, the moisture on which the hurricane engine feeds. Our current forecast is that we are five years into a 20 to 25 year cycle of increased hurricane activity.

Jerry Jarrell, Director of the National Hurricane Centre until his retirement in 2000

Future forecasts

D

Activity

Shelley Behnken's diary is available on the web at:

via www.heinemann.co.uk/hotlinks

Use this address to find more examples of how normal life was thrown into turmoil.

E *Here is the weather forecast for the next 25 years!*

Activity

In **Source D**, Jerry Jarrell mentions El Niño. Find out what it is.

Atmospheric Science is incredibly complicated. Most people are content with being told what *the impact* of major meteorological events will be. The cartoon in **Source E** sums up the warnings given by experts. Why are such simplistic headlines dangerous? Should such headlines be encouraged? Discuss this in groups.

Think of other issues that you study in geography, where the headlines warn of a difficult future. Present the headlines to your class and discuss why headlines over-simplify any issue.

Case study: Lee County, Florida

Responding to the hurricane hazard – a problem-solving exercise

The information given on page 20 suggested that we have little or no control over the occurrence of extreme weather events such as hurricanes. Problem solving is limited to how people react to the event and how individuals and organisations reduce the impact on the communities affected.

> **A** In this case study, the focus is on the State of Florida in the south-east of the US (see **Source A**). Your task is to suggest how one district of Florida, Lee County, should react to the potential hurricane hazard. Consider how any reaction would impact on:
> - long-term residents
> - new businesses wanting to set up in the area
> - local estate agents.

The issue for the planners in Lee County is clear:

- Hurricane events are forecast to increase in the next 25 years, according to some experts.
- Florida is one of the states in the direct path of Atlantic-based hurricanes.
- The area has experienced several hurricanes during the twentieth century.
- Lee County has experienced significant growth in recent years. The population and business is booming.
- Many local people suggest that existing plans for coping with the threat of a hurricane are inadequate.

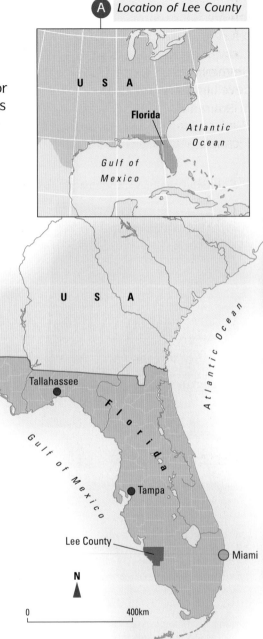

A Location of Lee County

A booming economy

Business has followed the same pattern of growth as the population. In recent years, the economy of Florida has boomed. It is one of the top five states for inward investment of new businesses. **Source B** shows four of the new arrivals to Lee County in the last five years.

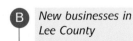

B New businesses in Lee County

Name of company	Line of business	Number employed
Sony	Electronics	600
G.E.	Accountants	540
Sims Intertech	Medical equipment	330
Gartners	Info. Technology	220

New homes

The combination of a natural population increase with the migration of people into the area, means that a significant number of new homes are required. Throughout Lee County, developers are offering new homes for sale. Many of them are on luxury developments such as the Palm Isles Development. **Source E** shows the location of this development. Notice how the waterfront location is in a vulnerable area should a hurricane strike. The location of the new Gartner Information Technology Centre is also shown.

> **Q**
> 1 What do you notice about the location of Fort Myers and Cape Coral?
>
> 2 Why do people in search of a new home often ignore potential hazards?

Background information: a rising population

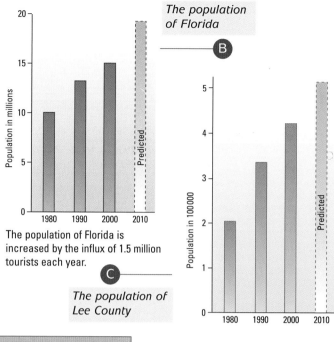

The population of Florida ● B

The population of Florida is increased by the influx of 1.5 million tourists each year. ● C

The population of Lee County

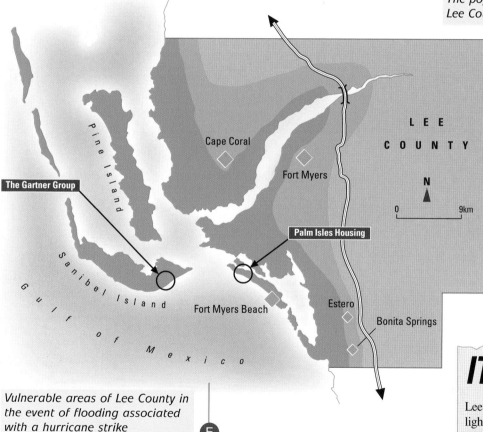

The Gartner Group

Palm Isles Housing

Vulnerable areas of Lee County in the event of flooding associated with a hurricane strike ● E

Key

Following a hurricane – risk of flooding due to stormsurge

- Low risk
- At risk
- High risk

Plans for Estero and Bonita Springs ● F

Plans for the area around Estero and Bonita Springs were announced in 1998. Details are given in the news article in **Source F**. As with the Palm Isles Development, it seems that the most prized areas are those in vulnerable locations shown in **Source E**. New residents appear to care more about their views and the availability of services than they do about a flood hazard.

In response to the news article, several existing residents wrote letters of concern. Three are given in **Source G** on the next page.

IT'S BOOM TIME!

Lee County Commissioners have given the green light to a number of major planning proposals which will bring further investment into the south of the County.

The 'Brooks' scheme will mean the construction of 5 200 homes and 250,000 square feet of business opportunity in Estero.

A 700 000 square foot shopping mall and a new 7 900 seat hockey stadium will be built at the junction of route 865 and inter-state highway 75. These proposals indicate our desire to share in the growth taking place throughout Florida.

Local objections to further development

Letters to the Editor

Development plans for Lee County

SIR – I will send the Commissioners an article I've just read about the increased hurricane threat. Are they aware that the proposals are planned for an area known to be at risk if there is a storm surge?...

SIR – I look forward to the Commissioners keeping their promise of a new hurricane shelter for the residents of Fort Myers Beach. Money should be no object now ...

SIR – As a resident of Bonita Beach, can the Commissioners tell me which evacuation route I should take when I find route 865 blocked by traffic? This new development is bound to put pressure on the roads ...

G *Letters to the local newspaper*

So what next?

Lee County officials will have difficult decisions to make about future development sites. All the existing plans to reduce the impact of a hurricane involve spending money! When the sums involved are huge, there is an argument for gambling, i.e. do nothing. After all, you may be lucky, the track of the hurricane could miss you. The experts may be wrong; there may be fewer hurricanes in the future.

Money to reduce the impact could be spent by three separate groups. Should...

- individuals take the responsibility?
- the national government take the responsibility?
- the State of Florida take responsibility?

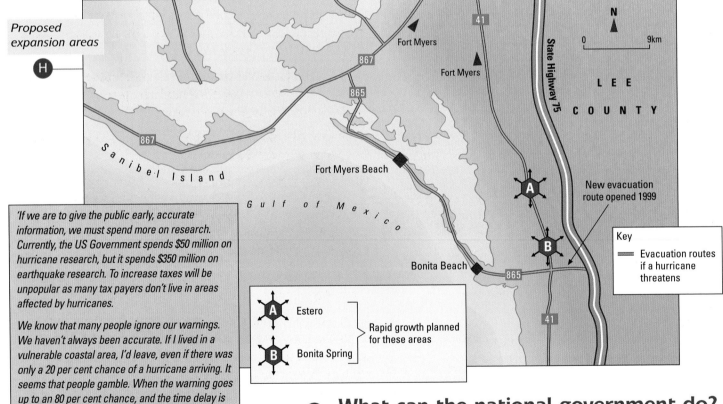

Proposed expansion areas

H

'If we are to give the public early, accurate information, we must spend more on research. Currently, the US Government spends $50 million on hurricane research, but it spends $350 million on earthquake research. To increase taxes will be unpopular as many tax payers don't live in areas affected by hurricanes.

We know that many people ignore our warnings. We haven't always been accurate. If I lived in a vulnerable coastal area, I'd leave, even if there was only a 20 per cent chance of a hurricane arriving. It seems that people gamble. When the warning goes up to an 80 per cent chance, and the time delay is only 2 hours, they panic, but it's too late!'

Stephen Leatherman, Director of the National Hurricane Centre

A Estero
B Bonita Spring
Rapid growth planned for these areas

Key
— Evacuation routes if a hurricane threatens

New evacuation route opened 1999

I

Q 1 Why do people ignore warnings?

Activity Discuss in groups who you think has the greatest responsibility to spend money reducing the effect of a hurricane.

What can the national government do?

Through agencies such as the National Weather Bureau (NWB) and the National Hurricane Centre (NHC), the Government based in Washington DC provides money for research into hurricane warnings. *Early warnings save lives*. By tracking a storm out in the Atlantic, the NWB is able to broadcast radio warnings at six-hour intervals. The public is told of the percentage chance of a hurricane passing within 65 miles of their home. The likely strength of the hurricane is also given.

Responding to the hurricane hazard

The role of local government

Most people look to the State and County Government for action in reducing the hurricane hazard. This responsibility is taken seriously, but authorities have a dilemma. Plans to reduce the hurricane hazard may require a rise in local taxes or the need to restrict people's freedom. Both may need to be implemented ahead of an election and could be unpopular with the voters.

What can the individual citizen do?

 The options for Lee County

> It can refuse planning permission in vulnerable areas (e.g. low lying coastal zones). This goes against a natural desire to see inward investment into an area, with the increased rates that will be collected.

> It can designate certain buildings (e.g. schools) as public shelters. This costs a great deal of money as the building must be built to a high specification and be kept ready for emergencies at all times.

> When new roads are planned, state authorities are aware of the need to plan safe and efficient escape routes. Roads need to be wide and built without bottlenecks such as junctions. The extra cost is huge.

I've spent a fortune protecting myself. I know of some families who simply can't afford these things. My purpose-built hurricane shelter cost $1 000 and I've taken out an additional loan of $20,000 over 10 years to fit storm shutters and have my roof strengthened.

It's crazy, isn't it? I've received a letter from my insurance company, saying my premiums are being doubled. An expert has told the company of an increased hurricane threat in the future.

Really? I attended a 'hurricane awareness lecture' at the University of Florida. It was useful, but they charged $65. It only lasted an hour!

What would you do?

When the news of a major development for Estero and Bonita Springs was announced, it was clear to Lee County officials that local opinion was divided. Soon there would be another planning proposal, and Lee County was bound to attract further investment. As decision makers, they would be pulled in many directions. They know that:

• There is an increased hurricane risk in the future. Residents had complained that existing hurricane precautions were inadequate. What would the future hold?

• Improving hurricane precautions would cost a great deal. Local people would have to pay.

• Making the wrong decisions (e.g. to restrict planning permission in vulnerable areas), means future inward investment could be jeopardised. Companies would probably go elsewhere. This would cost jobs and the County would lose valuable business rates.

• Elections will be held in three years. They want to remain popular with the voters.

A team of **consultants** was called in to advise the planning officials in Lee County. The consultants produced a detailed document to help the officials decide on a medium-term strategy. A summary document was produced.

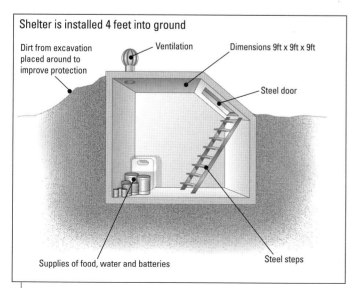

Shelter is installed 4 feet into ground

Dirt from excavation placed around to improve protection
Ventilation
Dimensions 9ft x 9ft x 9ft
Steel door
Steel steps
Supplies of food, water and batteries

C *A standard hurricane shelter*

Activity

Use the summary document in **Source D** on the next page as if you were a planning officer for Lee County. What options would you take up? *Justify your answer* based on the information you have gained by reading this chapter.

There is no correct answer, just a well argued answer. To help you, each 'option for the future' has been given a score:

1 = Certain to happen   3 = May happen
2 = Likely to happen   4 = Unlikely to happen

Which options would you choose? Justify your answer.

D *Options for the future – a summary*

	Will save lives	Taxes will go up	Investment will be lost
Evacuation routes Construct more highways to link with off-shore islands and widen routes that lead away from the coast. The most recent project near Bonita Springs was a small-scale project, but still cost $950 000.	2	1	4
Public shelters Build two new shelters. Current estimates suggest that existing shelters are inadequate. Some 30 000 people would not be able to be accommodated. The last project of this kind cost $1 million, where Lee County subsidised the building of a new ice-hockey stadium. This doubles up as a shelter in times of emergency.	1	1	4
Refuse planning permission No new houses or business development would be allowed in areas known to be vulnerable to storm waves or floods associated with hurricanes.	2	4	1
Strict controls Refuse planning permission unless houses and business properties meet strict building regulations. Hurricane shelters must be included, ground floor elevations must be one metre above known flood levels. Shutters must be fitted, roofs reinforced.	2	4	2
Subsidised loans Offer existing residents low-cost loans. Money must be spent on strengthening existing properties with storm shutters and strengthening roofs. Hurricane shelters can be built.	3	3	4
Promote individual responsibility All Lee County citizens are given advice on private insurance. Leaflets issued to show householders how to prepare for the arrival of a hurricane (emergency rations, etc.). Maps issued to show the most vulnerable areas. Subsidised 'Alert radios' for sale. These cut in when a hurricane alert is issued.	3	4	4
Nationwide campaign Commit the County to a five-year campaign for increased national spending on hurricane research. A team of three staff would liaise with other counties and States to persuade the Washington Government to invest in the NWB and the NHC.	3	4	4

Review point

Consider the route through this chapter.

 Not only can extreme weather events can be inconvenient, they can be killers. There are many examples in the US.

 In the past, people have reacted to the event, rather than planned for it.

 Today, we tend to plan for the event. However, opinion is often divided as to what should be done.

Your opinion is valid, as long as you can *justify* it. There is a skill to justification.

3

Damming the River Yangtze

River processes create different landforms and affect people's activities. River landforms can be tourist attractions and provide fertile farmland. Rivers can be used for transporting goods and people and they are a source of fresh water for settlements and economic activity. They are a valuable resource for people worldwide, but they can also be hazardous. Either way, rivers need careful management in order benefit people.

In this unit, you will be asked to consider the following questions:

* What do rivers do?
* How do rivers benefit people and how can they cause problems?
* What are the costs and benefits of the Three Gorges Dam?
* How can the scheme be managed to minimise the negative effects and maximise the positive effects on people's activities?

You will then be asked to make a decision about whether the new dam on the Yangtze is a good idea. You must try to minimise its impact.

What do rivers do?

Water is constantly cycled between the oceans, the land and the atmosphere. Water evaporates from the sea; it forms clouds when it cools and condenses from vapour to water droplets, and eventually falls as precipitation, before returning to the sea. This **hydrological cycle** is shown in **Source B**. Rain that falls on land will collect in one of the world's many **drainage basins** shown in **Source A**. The rainwater is held in different water **stores**:

- lakes
- soil
- rock
- vegetation
- rivers

There are important **transfers** between the stores:

- evaporation into the atmosphere
- condensation from vapour
- precipitation to the ground
- infiltration, percolation, throughflow and groundwater flow
- surface flow and river flow

Rivers are the most important transfer of water from the land stores to the sea. A river channel is also a water store, since it can take days or weeks for water to flow from a river source to its mouth.

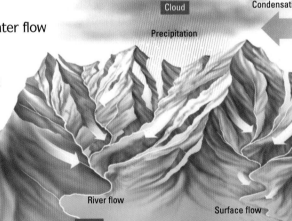

A A world map of major drainage basins

B Hydrological cycle of a drainage basin

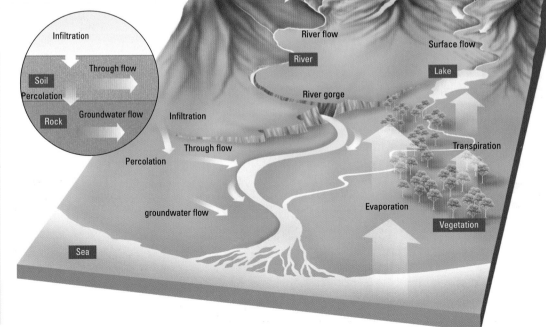

Q River discharge varies.
1 Why do some rivers discharge more water than others?
2 Why does a river's discharge vary over a year?
3 If there is more water in a river, how will this affect erosion, transportation and deposition?
4 If there is less water in the river, how will processes and landforms be affected?

Source D lists eight of the world's rivers. Precipitation falls in a river's **catchment area**. Each river collects this fresh water from different stores and drains it into the sea. This water is called the river **discharge** and is measured in cubic metres (per second). As the river flows downstream, it performs three different processes:

- **erosion** - **transportation**
- **deposition**

As **Source C** shows, rocks and soils are **eroded**, and many tonnes of this sediment are transported downstream by the river. The sediment is then **deposited**, either along the course of the river, or at the river mouth. This deposition occurs whenever the river slows down (loses energy) and cannot carry as much sediment. Deposition might be on a bend in the channel, when the river floods onto its flood plain, or when the river flows into a lake or the sea.

Bigger rivers can usually transport more sediment, but **Sources D** and **E** show that this is not always true. Other factors will influence how much soil and rock is eroded in the river's catchment area. The water and sediment are valuable for a range of human activities, as well as having an important role in the natural environment. The sediment makes deposition landforms such as islands, deltas and flood plains.

C · Erosion, transportation and deposition

Erosion

❶ Hydraulic Action
❷ Abrasion
❸ Attrition

The sheer force of water dislodges particles

These stones in turn dislodge other particles

The particles themselves are worn down as they travel downstream

Transportation

❶ Bedload
❷ Suspended load
❸ Solution

Larger rocks and pebbles

Tiny particles

Sediment that dissolves

Deposition

❶ Deposition on flood plain when river breaks its banks

❷ Meander bar

❸ Delta at river mouth

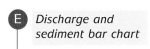

D — River discharge

River	Sediment (million tonnes per year)	Average discharge at river mouth (cu metres per second)	Length (km)	Drainage basin area ('000 sq km)
Nile	300	1584	6584	2881
Amazon	450	180000	6516	7180
Yangtze	600	35000	6300	1970
Mississippi	350	17545	6019	3221
Huang He	1000	1365	4845	745
Zaire	500	42000	4700	3822
Brahmaputra	850	20000	2900	938
Ganges	1600	15000	2700	1073

E · Discharge and sediment bar chart

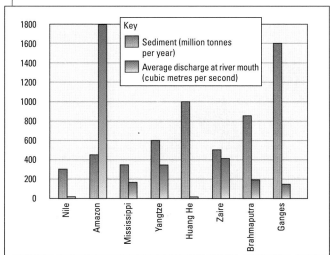

Key
- Sediment (million tonnes per year)
- Average discharge at river mouth (cubic metres per second)

Q
1 Why do some rivers erode, transport and deposit more sediment than others?

2 'The bigger the river, the more sediment it carries'. Is this hypothesis correct? Explain your answer.

3 What other links (relationships) would you expect between the columns in **Source D**? Test your hypothesis with a graph. You could use a spreadsheet programme (like Excel) to do a scattergraph.

4 Choose another river and investigate the problem of erosion and deposition through www.heinemann.co.uk/hotlinks

Is the River Yangtze a benefit or a problem for China?

The Yangtze River is 6 300km in length, the biggest river in China, the longest in Asia and the third longest in the world. The river has hundreds of tributaries in its 1 970 000km² drainage basin. Its whole catchment area covers one fifth of China's total land area. **Source B** shows its location, and **Source C** gives details of the benefits and problems caused by this great river.

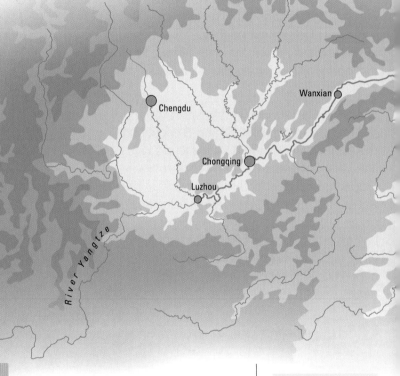

A   *Facts about the Yangtze*

Source of river:	The Qinghai-Tibet Plateau, a mountainous area of snow and ice, 4900m above sea level
Length of river:	6300km
Population in the drainage basin:	400 million people live in the Yangtze catchment area
Average discharge:	34,000 cubic metres per second

The river is a major tourist attraction. The most beautiful section, the Three Gorges (narrow limestone canyons, some 200km long), provides some of the most stunning scenery in China and attracts many foreign visitors each year.

For thousands of years, the silt from the river has been deposited on the flood plain. The Yangtze basin is the 'granary of China', growing 70 per cent of the country's rice harvest and half of China's food production. Barley, wheat, corn and cotton are all important crops grown on the fertile flood plain. There is a very high population density on the flood plain.

B   *Benefits and drawbacks of the Yangtze River*

The Yangtze is one of world's busiest rivers. Thousands of boats carry passengers and cargo along its course. Deep water allows ocean-going ships to sail upstream as far as Wuhan, 1 100km inland.

Q   What are the economic benefits of the River Yangtze?

- primary industry
- secondary industry
- tertiary industry

Several hydroelectric power plants – like this one at Gezhou Dam – use the flow of the river to generate electricity.

Chongqing (15 million people) is one of the biggest cities in the world. The river provides water for this – and other – cities. It is also a drainage outlet for effluent from industry and housing.

Water from the river irrigates crops and provides a supply of fresh water for millions of people in the Yangtze catchment area.

Navigating the river is very dangerous, especially through the Three Gorges section when water levels are low. When the river is in flood, it flows dangerously fast.

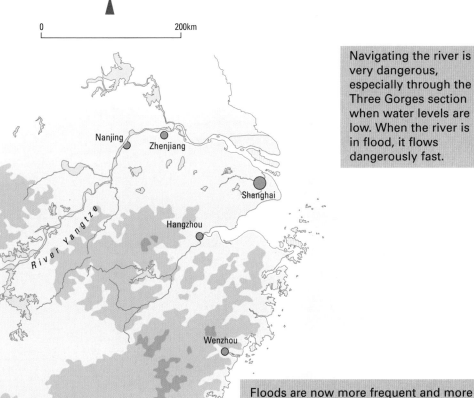

N

0   200km

Nanjing
Zhenjiang
Shanghai
Yichang
Wuhan
Hangzhou
River Yangtze
Changsha
Wenzhou

Key
Land over 3000m
1000 – 3000m
200 – 1000m
Land under 200m

Floods are now more frequent and more disastrous because:
- more people now live in the river valley, so greater numbers are at risk
- 85 per cent of the Yangtze basin's original forest cover has been removed. This deforestation has reduced water stores and infiltration
- intense development of industry and housing has decreased infiltration and increased surface run off.

C *Flood deaths in the twentieth century*

Floods on the Yangtze killed more than 300 000 people in the twentieth century, with many more dying from starvation which followed from crop failure in the flood plain.
- *The worst floods were in 1931, when 140 000 people died.*
- *In 1954, some 30,000 people died.*
The most serious floods in recent years were in 1998. Then 14 million people were made homeless, 5 million houses were destroyed, 25 million hectares of farmland were affected, $20 billion worth of damage was caused and more than 3000 people died.

Q 1 What problems need solving?
- Why are problems now worse than in the past?
- Which problems are made worse by *low* water levels, and which problems are caused by *high* river levels?

2 Explain why this makes planning difficult.

3 How can river flow be controlled?

How can water surplus and deficit be managed?

The discharge from the Yangtze is shown in **Source A**. Over time, the amount of water that falls in a catchment area is exactly equal to the amount of water that is lost *out* of the catchment area. Water comes in as precipitation, and it can escape through the river or as vapour into the air (see **Source B**). This is called 'Water Balance'. The inputs and outputs do not always balance. Sometimes more water comes in than out. This is **water surplus**. At other times of the year, there is not enough water coming into the river. This is **water deficit**.

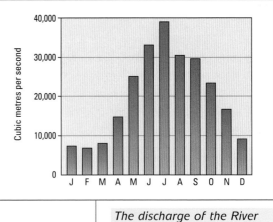

A   *The discharge of the River Yangtze over a year*

Q
1 Explain why water surplus will be a problem at some times of the year.
2 Explain why water deficit might be a problem at other times of the year.

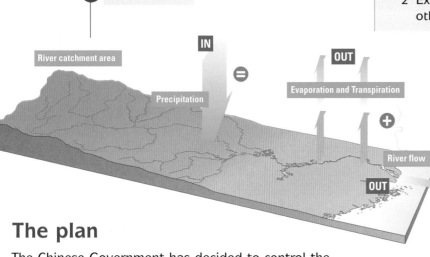

B   *Water balance*

The plan

The Chinese Government has decided to control the River Yangtze with a massive scheme: **The Three Gorges Dam** (See **Sources C, D, E** and **F**).

This water management scheme is attempting to solve the problems of:

- floods
- dangerous navigation
- irregular water supply.

The new dam will bring many benefits, but there will also be problems. It will change the river flow, and will therefore change the river's processes and its landforms.

The **Three Gorges Dam** will not only be the largest and most powerful dam ever built anywhere in the world, it will also be the world's largest construction project. It is said to be 'the biggest, most expensive and most hazardous of all HEP projects on this planet'.

Start date:	1993
Completion date:	2009
The dam:	2km wide 186m high
The reservoir:	600km 39.3 billion cubic metres capacity
Power station:	26 generators 18 200 megawatts
Estimated cost:	over $20 billion (may be as much as $75 billion)

C   *Project statistics*

Q
3 Why is the Three Gorges Dam being constructed? Organise your answer under these headings:
- Benefits for people living near the Yangtze
- Benefits for China and its government

The massive concrete dam will control the river at the point shown in **Source D**. It will create a 600km long lake behind the dam.

Passenger and cargo ships will pass through a system of locks to get past the dam (**Source F**).

Q 4 The dam will regulate river flow, stop flooding downstream and prevent the transportation of silt. Explain how this will affect:
- river flow downstream
- the flood plain downstream

Map of the Three Gorges Dam along the River Yangtze **E**

Site of the Three Gorges Dam **D**

Dachang
Yunanzhen
Yungang
Fengjie
Wushan
Zigui
Badong
Three Gorges Dam
Xintan
Wanxian
Qutang Gorge
Wu Gorge
Sandouping
Gezhou Dam
Yichang
Xiling Gorge
Wulingzhen
Zhongxian
Zhicheng

HEP station
Ship locks raise ships 160 metres to lake
Lake
Yangtze
Ship lift (small boats)

F *The dam and locks*

G *China's president visiting the site*

Q 5 What stage has the construction now reached? There are lots of up-to-date web sites on this project. Search on the Internet by using a phrase such as 'Three Gorges Dam'.

6 This project has been compared with the Great Wall of China. Why then do you think that China's government is so keen to undertake this project?

What will be the benefits of the scheme?

Activity

Will the 'benefits' of the Three Gorges Dam outweigh its 'costs'?
Organize the effects into a table of 'costs' and 'benefits':

	Benefits	Costs
Economic		
Social		
Environmental		

Not all the effects are equal in importance. In order to weigh them up, you should give each one a 'weighting' or score, as follows:

1 = not very important
2 = quite important
3 = lots of damage or benefit to lots of people
4 = serious effects
5 = very damaging or very beneficial

Then add the cost and benefits to judge the scheme for yourself.

 A *The Three Gorges Dam and lake*

Farmland
60 000 hectares of fertile farmland will be flooded and 600 000 farmers will have to move.

National pride and prestige
It is the greatest project in China since the Great Wall was started, over 2000 years ago.

Wanxian
Two-thirds of the city will be flooded. Some 900 factories and 250 000 people will have to move. The city will be more accessible: there will be a new international airport, a new main road and – for the first time – a railway.

Wanxian
River Yangtze
Zigui
Gezhou Dam
Three Gorges Dam
Yichang
Zhijiang
Fuling
N
0   50km
Fengdu

Key
☐ Area to be flooded (approximate)

Chongqing
River Yangtze

Chongqing
Boats that are 10 times bigger than at present will be able to navigate the river. The city of Chongqing (15 million people) at the head of the new lake will become the world's biggest seaport, taking ocean-going ships from the Pacific Ocean.

People
1.2 million people will need rehousing: 2 cities (Wanxian has 300,000 inhabitants), 11 major towns, 114 smaller towns, 1711 villages. The quality of life in the surrounding regions is – at present – below China's national average (illiteracy rate is 2.5 per cent above average).

The lake
The new lake will offer opportunities for recreational and tourist developments. It will provide the basis for a huge fishing industry.

... and what will be the costs of the scheme?

Sediment
Sediment will be trapped in the lake, instead of flowing downstream. It will eventually silt up the harbour at Chongqing and ruin the HEP turbines. The river downstream will flow faster and will transport less sediment for depositional landforms.

Pollution
There are more than 3000 factories in the Three Gorges area, discharging around 1 billion tonnes of waste water (8380 tonnes pollutants) each year, 90 per cent of which is untreated. The quality of river water is a serious threat to the ecology and human health at low flow conditions. Pollutants from domestic waste, factories and farmland are steadily increasing. Some estimates suggest that 68 per cent of all nitrates added to the soils are leached into the river waters. In future, this will enter the lake. A total of 250 billion gallons of raw sewage per year will make the lake a big sewer.

The river
Water flow will be regulated all year round. Total discharge at the river mouth will be the same, but during the dry season the water levels will be nearly doubled upstream of the dam. Water will be deep through the Three Gorges.

Qu

Badong

Yungyang

Jialing

Wanxian

Zigui

Fu

Yichang

Shashi

Zhong Xian

Fengdu

Lake Chang

Changshou

B

Chonqing

Ecosystems
Sediment will be trapped in the new lake. There are 40 unique species of fish in the Three Gorges section of the Yangtze and 36 rare plant species. Downstream, the rare Chinese river dolphin lives in the silt-laden river bed of the Yangtze. There are only 100 river dolphins.

Local climate
The lake will change the local climate, making it cooler in summer and warmer in winter. It is expected that fruit production will expand in the more moderate climate.

C

Religious, cultural and archaeological sites
828 important cultural sites will be flooded, including tombs of ancient Chinese leaders and important Buddhist engravings. Thousands of important archaeological sites along the river valley will be lost for ever.

Power
The HEP station will generate electricity equivalent to 18 nuclear power stations, 14 per cent of China's power, reducing coal burning (in power stations) by 50 million tonnes per year (and CO_2 emissions by 100 million tonnes). However, the electricity will have to be transmitted across China to other cities. A massive new electricity grid will have to be built.

What's the issue?

China is still – by far – the most populated country in the world. In 1949, when China became a communist country, the vast majority of people lived in total poverty. Since then, China has developed its economy and steadily improved its standards of living, but it is still an LEDC. One government policy has been called 'the modernisations', where improvements have been made to the economy, but in the past these developments were often done:

• at the expense of local people
• without regard for the natural environment
• without help from foreign countries.

In order to complete the Three Gorges Project, China needs:

• equipment and technical help from MEDCs
• money to finance the scheme.

However, MEDCs will not support the scheme if there is opposition in their own countries. Businesses must be sure that they are making a good investment that will not have too many negative effects.

> **Q** 1 Why do some people support the Project and other people oppose it?
>
> 2 Are some opinions more important than others?
>
> 3 Can we generalise about what groups of people will think?

A Some opinions on the issue

Farmers will be a problem. They are uneducated and lack skills, so they will not be able to find jobs in other businesses, but they cannot be allowed to stand in the way of progress. China's economy needs to develop, so that we can have better living standards for everyone in the twenty-first century.

We have decided to give them money to help them resettle, but it is up to them to find somewhere that will accept their family.

Government official

Unemployment in the Three Gorges area hovers around 11 per cent and if all money-losing, polluting enterprises are shut down as ordered, unemployment could jump to 70 per cent. That would throw tens of thousands of people out of work and create havoc for local governments.

British journalist

For me, it is terrible, but for my children, it will be wonderful. We'll have a fish farm by the reservoir and maybe set up a restaurant. We must make sacrifices for the good of the country.

Village resident forced to move

It's a pity that so much fertile land will be lost. We have farmed here for generations, but we don't know where we'll be moved, or even when. Any new farmland will not be as good as ours, especially if it is up the hill. I don't know how much compensation the government will give us. You cannot argue. You just take what they offer.

The big problem is corruption. Most of the money that is supposed to go to people is being taken by local villages and towns to 'improve' the place for new settlers.

Poor farmer forced to move

The Three Gorges Project

The birth of a vast lake among spectacular mountains will only add to the beauty of the Three Gorges. Once completed, the Three Gorges Project will itself become a new wonder of the world.

The giant dam will stand downstream to hold back Wushan mountain's clouds and rain. The hydropower station, as dazzling as a palace, will shoot out its mighty current through an extensive power grid.

The Three Gorges Dam

Like the Yellow Emperor not far from the dam, the modern building complexes are bound to draw flocks of travellers from all over the world.

China probably has more potential to develop HEP than any other country in the world. So far, we have only developed 10 per cent of that potential.

Engineer

Brochure on the Three Gorges Project **B**

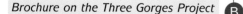

Making decisions

Your task

You work for a Canadian company that is interested in lending money to finance the Three Gorges Project. You must write a report in two parts.

Part 1:

Your decision

You are asked to use your cost-benefit analysis of the scheme to present a report to your parent company. On balance, do you think that the Three Gorges Project is a benefit for China and its people? You must *write a report* to your own boss, explaining whether the company should support the development, or not, and *justify* your decision with reasons.

My decision

- My summary of 'costs':
  Economic   Social   Environmental

- My summary of 'benefits':
  Economic   Social   Environmental

'On balance, I think that our company should ...'
'The main reason for my decision is that ...'
'The most important priority must be to ...'
'Although the dam ...'
'In the short term, the dam will ... but in the longer term it will ...'

Part 2:

Your recommendations

What should the Chinese government do to ensure that the dam and lake do not cause too many problems? Make some recommendations for the Chinese government, and include the following issues:

- moving people
- protecting the natural environment
- improving the quality of life of people in the flood area.

You could do this report as an oral presentation.

My recommendations

Use the following words and phrases in your recommendations:

- sustainable
- multiplier effect
- conserve
- exploit
- conflicts

The development of the Three Gorges Dam needs careful management, otherwise it will have a serious impact on people and the environment. I recommend that the Chinese government is asked to meet the following requirements:

- In order to minimize the negative impacts on the 12 million people who will have to move house, I suggest that ...
- The natural environment will be greatly affected by the lake and by the dam blocking the river flow. I suggest that ...
- At present, the 'quality of life' of local people is below the national average for China. In order to maximise the positive impacts of the scheme, I suggest that ...

Q 1 People clearly have different opinions and will weigh up the 'costs' and 'benefits' differently, according to how they are affected and their perception of the advantages.

   a Think of three other groups of people who would support the Project and three groups of people who would oppose it. Explain your answer.

   b Which people in China are more likely to influence the decision-making process? Explain your answer.

2 Many Chinese peasants in the area to be flooded are poor and illiterate. Imagine that you are a Chinese government official. You have to explain to them why they must move house.

   a Prepare a short speech that you would make in a local village or

   b produce a poster that explains the benefits of the dam to the village.

Review exercise

Draw your own annotated sketch map to summarize the facts about this case study of a water management scheme. Use the planning boxes to organize your work.

The Three Gorges project:
Fact file
• What?
• Where?
• When?
• How?

The problems that needed solving:
• floods
• low living standards

Costs of the scheme:
• impact on people
• effects on the natural environment – ecosystems, hydrological processes and landforms
• impact on the economy (primary, secondary and tertiary employment)

Benefits of the scheme:
• floods and river flow downstream
• transportation
• economic advantages for some places and some industry
• advantages for certain groups of people

4

Battling to save our coasts

There rolls the deep where grew the tree.
O earth, what changes hast thou seen
There where the long street roars hath been
the stillness of the central sea.

Alfred, Lord Tennyson
in memorium A.H.H. CXXII

All across the world, people's land, homes, activities and even their lives are under the threat of attack from one of nature's greatest forces – the sea. Thousands of hectares of land are washed away each year, as day after day the sea pounds and pummels our coastlines.

In some places, this erosion continues unchecked. In others, particularly where there is human activity, people battle against the threat by designing different schemes to try to slow down or stop the erosion and its impact.

In this unit, you will be asked to consider the following questions:

• What is happening along the Holderness coast?
• What processes are contributing to erosion along the Holderness coast?
• What is the impact of erosion on people and the environment?
• How can erosion and its impact be managed?
• How successful is this management?

You will then be asked to investigate the Holderness Coastline in north-east England. This is one of the most rapidly eroding coasts in Europe. You will conclude your investigation by writing a report justifying your plans for managing part of the Holderness Coastline.

What is happening along the Holderness coast?

A *The lost villages of the Holderness coast*

Holderness is the name given to a stretch of coastline in the East Riding of Yorkshire. It is 61km long, stretching from Flamborough Head in the north to Spurn Point in the south.

The coastline of Holderness is eroding by about 2m per year. The erosion occurs mainly during storms and high tides. In October 1967, a loss of 6m was recorded over two days at Barmston.

Since Roman times, more than 30 villages and 3km of coastline have 'disappeared' into the sea .

I own a caravan site at Withernsea. When I walked around the site this morning, I couldn't believe what I saw. Over 4m of land had been washed away overnight. The fish and chip shop is now just 2m from the edge of the cliffs, two months ago it was 13m away. When I took over the site four years ago, there were two chalets between the shop and the cliffs.

Local property owner **B**

C *Chalets at risk from cliff erosion*

Map labels: Scarborough, Site of Holbeck Hall Hotel, North Sea, Flamborough Head, Bridlington, Barmston, Holderness, Mappleton, Hull, Withernsea, Humber Estuary, Spurn Point

N

0   10km

Key
- Erosion
- Deposition
- Transportation

Q 1 What is happening along the Holderness coast?

2 Why does the Holderness coastline erode so rapidly?

Why is the coast eroding so rapidly?

There are several reasons which help to explain why the coastline is eroding so rapidly.

- The cliffs along the Holderness coast are made from 'glacial till' – sometimes called 'boulder clay' because of the large stones and boulders found in it. This rock, which was deposited by ice sheets, is very soft and easily eroded by the force of the waves.
- The high tides produce strong powerful waves.
- The beaches along the coast are very narrow and offer little protection to the cliffs. The sand on the beaches is continually being washed southwards by the coastal currents. This is called 'longshore drift'.
- The chalk headland of Flamborough Head prevents the transport of beach-building materials to the Holderness beaches.

What processes are changing the coastline?

There are three processes affecting the Holderness coastline: erosion, transportation (see below) and deposition (see p. 44).

Erosion

There are two main erosive processes: **abrasion** and **hydraulic action**.

- Abrasion (see **Source A**): Stones and pebbles carried by the waves repeatedly bash against the soft rock of the cliffs (1). Over time this causes a groove to be cut into the base of the cliff (2). This is called **undercutting**. This groove eventually becomes so large and deep (3) that the cliff above collapses, causing the cliff to **recede** (4).

- Hydraulic action: The power of the waves hitting the cliff forces air into cracks in the cliff face. Under pressure the air expands and weakens the surrounding rock, causing it eventually to break away.

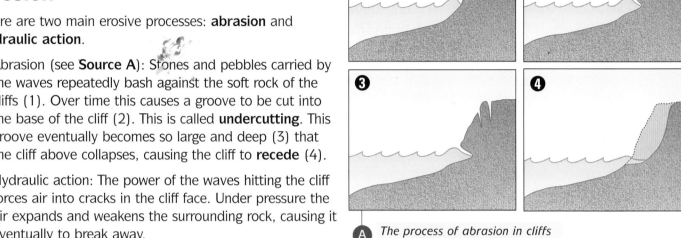

A *The process of abrasion in cliffs*

Q How does erosion lead to cliff collapse and the formation of a new cliff profile? Draw labelled diagrams to show this.

Weathering

It is not only the waves that cause the cliffs to wear away. The wind and rain also affect the stability of the cliffs. After heavy rainfall, the clay cliffs become waterlogged and very heavy. This can lead to large areas of cliffs slipping down towards the beach. This is called **slumping**.

Transportation

Material that is eroded from the cliffs and beaches is washed in a southwards direction along the coast by a process called **longshore drift** (see **Source B**).

The wind blows the waves towards the beach at an angle. Grains of sand at A are moved up the beach to point B by the **swash** at the same angle. However, they are pulled back down the beach by the **backwash** to point C. The backwash follows the natural slope of the beach. Another wave picks up the grains of sand at C and carries them to D, and the backwash then pulls them down to E. This continuous process causes the sand grains to move along the beach and the coast in what is known as a **sawtooth pattern**.

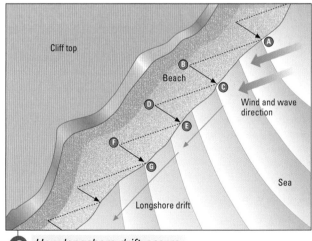

C *How longshore drift occurs*

Activity

Find out more about transportation. Useful addresses can be found at www.heinemann.co.uk/hotlinks.

How is deposition changing the coastline?

Although erosion and transportation are the main processes affecting the Holderness Coastline, deposition also plays an important part in making new landforms. Coastal deposition occurs when the sea currents lose energy and their capacity for carrying sediment is reduced. This frequently happens where river estuaries meet the sea. Both river flow and sea currents slow down and sediments are deposited to create landforms such as deltas and spits.

Along the Holderness coastline, deposition has formed a long spit called Spurn Point. This 5km long spit at the southern end of the Holderness coast has formed where the coastal currents (longshore drift) carrying sediment meet the river flow of the Humber estuary.

From historical accounts of settlements and lighthouses, particularly accounts of their destruction and the break-up of the spit, we now know that there have been five 'Spurn Points' over the last 1000 years. Each spit has grown until it has become unstable, been destroyed and then rebuilt slightly to the west of the former one, the cycles lasting approximately 250 years. The current spit is nearing the end of the cycle, and despite considerable coastal defences the neck is in continual danger of being breached.

A *Spurn Point – a depositional landform*

Activity

Find out about other depositional landforms such as deltas. If you have an Internet connection, use a search engine such as Metacrawler (www.metacrawler.com) and type 'delta+coast' into the text panel.

How is erosion impacting the lives of people?

We own a caravan park along Galleon Beach at Skipsea. Every year we've watched the sea take more of our land away. In 1993, we decided to do something about it. We asked the local council for help, but they could not afford to build any sea defences – so we built a sea wall ourselves. It cost £65 000 and it stretches for 65m. It is made from thick reinforced concrete and should last for years. Without it, we would have lost our caravan park as well as our house and we would have gone out of business.

Increasingly, business people along the coast are paying for protection schemes to help preserve their businesses. Two caravan sites, each situated on either end of the sea wall in the photograph, have now built their own sea walls (see 'Making Decisions', page 49). Jack Turton, managing director of the Batley-based Turton Group that owns the sites, stated: 'It will give us a minimum of ten extra years. To stay in business, we had to do something because the land was being lost at a rate of knots.'

Sea defences at Galleon Beach **B**

Q What impact will the building of these sea walls have on the tourists who stay at the caravan parks that the walls protect?

How can an eroding coastline be managed?

All along the Holderness coast, attempts have been made to stop or slow down the erosion that threatens people, their property and the environment. Some of these schemes, paid for by local and national government, have cost millions of pounds. Other schemes, such as those at Skipsea, have been paid for privately.

There are a number of ways in which the coast can be protected. Some are familiar and have been tried and tested throughout the world, while others are more experimental.

One method of protection is to build a 'hard barrier', such as a sea wall (Source **A**), out of reinforced concrete. In the 1980s such a wall was built to replace a damaged one at Hornsea, at a cost of £10 000 per metre.

Another type of hard barrier involves building groynes (Source **B**), at regular intervals along a beach. These large wooden structures help to slow down longshore drift.

Another method of coastal protection removes some of the energy of the waves. 'Rock armour' (Source **C**), is often used for this purpose. It not only breaks up the waves causing them to lose energy, but also provides a hard barrier. Rock armour is usually made of large granite blocks.

Some scientists have suggested that a 'reef' made of millions of concrete-filled tyres laid along the coast will also help to reduce the power of the sea.

A fourth way of protecting coastlines uses 'beach nourishment'. This is where eroded beach material is replaced. The sand must be at least as coarse as the sand that is eroding, or it will easily be washed away. If longshore drift is affecting the beach, groynes may also have to be built.

A fifth method, which is favoured by some scientists as the best solution, is to do nothing and let nature take its course.

A The new sea wall at Hornsea

B Groynes along Hornsea beach

C Rock armour at Hornsea

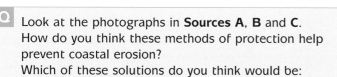

Q Look at the photographs in **Sources A**, **B** and **C**.
How do you think these methods of protection help prevent coastal erosion?
Which of these solutions do you think would be:

- most effective?
- best for the environment?

How successful is coastline management?

A case study of Mappleton

Mappleton is situated 3km south of Hornsea. It is a small village of approximately 50 properties. The main coastal road runs between the village and the sea following the line of the cliffs.

The cliffs at Mappleton have been eroding at a rate of 2m per year. This rapid erosion has threatened both the road and the village. In 1990, the road was only 50m from the cliff edge.

The same year, a decision was made by Holderness District Council to build sea defences to protect the coastal road, as this would be cheaper than re-building the road further inland.

The defences were successful: a higher sandy beach was formed as the rock groynes trapped sand and the rock barrier prevented the waves from eroding and undercutting the cliff.

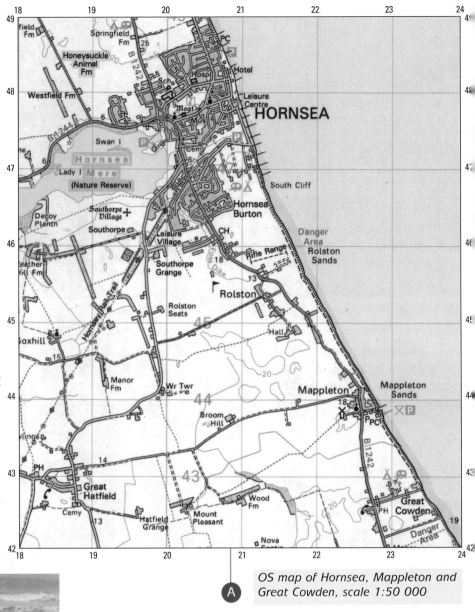

A OS map of Hornsea, Mappleton and Great Cowden, scale 1:50 000

B Local councillors visit the sea defences at Mappleton

What effects did these defences have on people living in and around Mappleton?

The villagers who live and work in Mappleton were very pleased when the sea defences were built because their properties and land had been protected.

However, people living along the coast to the north and south of Mappleton were not happy with the sea defences at all.

The beaches, particularly to the south, were starved of sand because the rock groynes were interrupting the process of longshore drift. Even faster cliff erosion was experienced in these areas leading to an increased loss of land.

Q With the aid of diagrams, explain how the sea defences at Mappleton helped to protect the coastline.

A case study of Great Cowden

The residents of Mappleton are secure thanks to the sea defences built in 1991, but just a few kilometres south, people in the sparsely populated farmland of Great Cowden are very unhappy. Sue Earle is one of those people. She lived in a house on Grange Farm (shown in **Source C**) in Great Cowden all her life. In 1996, she had to move.

- Why did this happen?
- Why was there no protection for this stretch of coastline?

> My Uncle John bought this farm in 1957. At that time, it was 90m from the cliff edge. When I had to leave in 1996, it was only 4m from the edge.
>
> We always knew we were fighting a losing battle with the sea, but since the defences at Mappleton were built the situation has got worse. The cliffs started eroding three times faster than before the defences were built.
>
> There is no help for people like us. The council won't build sea defences because there is only farmland here. They will only pay to protect roads and towns.
>
> We can't even claim compensation or insurance – because coastal erosion is classed as an act of God.

Cliff erosion at Great Cowden showing the threat to Grange Farm

C

D Sue Earle

Activity

Imagine that you are a resident of Great Cowden. Write a letter to a local newspaper explaining how you feel about the prospect of losing your home and livelihood.

Sue Earle and her Uncle John moved out of their farmhouse into a wooden chalet that they had converted from an old chicken broiler house. It is located half a mile from the sea.

Sue wonders how long it will be before they have to move again. They cannot afford to buy another house. To Sue, the future looks very bleak.

Sue has been working with other farmers and residents to try to force the council and government to provide them with compensation. She calls it relocation assistance because no one could compensate for everything that they are losing. So far, they have not been successful.

It is not only residents who live near unprotected stretches of coastline who are worried. Technical surveys have reported that repair work needs to be carried out on sea walls along 45 miles of the Holderness coastline.

Many residents are asking the question: 'Can the power of the sea be stopped?'

Some scientists believe the answer is: 'No. All the sea defence work is simply slowing down the inevitable – the complete removal of the present Holderness coastline.'

Coastline management involves tough decisions

People living and working along the Holderness coast share real concerns over the threats that the sea is making to their lives, homes, businesses and jobs.

In the larger towns, much money has been spent on coastal defences, but in the smaller villages and isolated rural areas very little coastal defence work has been done. Such work has nearly always been financed by the people themselves.

Each of the four people in **Source A** are affected in some way by the action of the sea. However, lots of other people are also affected – from local shopkeepers to the postal worker. For more examples, see **Source B** below.

A

Differing opinions

I'm sorry, but the local council, even with the help of EU funding, has only so much money to spend. We have to prioritise our efforts. The large towns with more people and businesses have the highest priority.

Representative of council

I live and work in Skipsea. My family owns a caravan site. In the last 10 years, we have lost over 50 pitches. Unless something is done, we'll go out of business.

Businessman

I am a lecturer at a nearby university. I have been studying this coastline for over 20 years. In my view, money spent on sea defences is wasted money. Nature should be left to take its course and the money should be spent on providing compensation for people who are badly affected.

University lecturer

This talk is all very well, but we need action. My farm is only 30m from the cliff edge. In a few years, it'll be gone. What will happen to my family and me then? That's what I want to know.

Farmer

B *Some people affected by the eroding coastline*

Activity

Make a list of people who you think would be affected in some way by the sea eroding the coastline. Beside each person, write down how you think they would be affected. You could write your answers in the form of a table as shown in the example below.

Person	How affected
Builder	May be asked to repair houses or even to help demolish those in danger of collapse
Farm worker	May lose job as farms close due to loss of land and property
Shopkeeper	May lose trade as people move away from the area

Making decisions

A coastal management consultancy has been approached by the owner of the caravan site in **Source A** to provide advice on what can be done to protect the site from further erosion. Twenty years ago, the cliff edge lay much further out. In another twenty years, the remainder of this site will have been lost to the sea

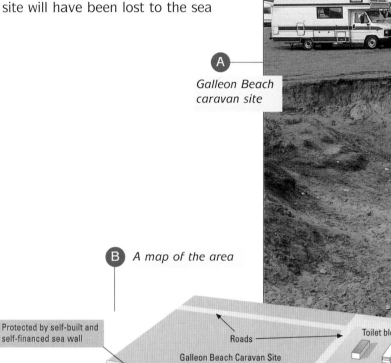

A Galleon Beach caravan site

B *A map of the area*

Protected by self-built and self-financed sea wall

Roads

Galleon Beach Caravan Site

Toilet block

Caravan pitches

Galleon Beach

Coastline to be managed

Sea

The caravan site owner has asked the coastal management consultants to:

1 Identify the different options that can be used to manage this stretch of coastline.

2 Prioritise these options in terms of effectiveness and cost.

3 Recommend and justify a course of action to be taken to manage the coast in front of the caravan site.

Activity

Imagine that you work for the coastal management consultancy. Using the material in the chapter and any information that have researched yourself, write a report for the owner of the caravan site. Make sure that you include the three things he has asked the consultancy to comment upon.

Review exercise

Processes

a In the context of the work on coastlines, briefly explain each of the following processes:

1 erosion
2 transportation
3 deposition.

b What is the difference between erosion and weathering?

c Use actual examples to describe and explain how each of the following processes help to create distinct landforms. Illustrate your answers with diagrams where appropriate.

1 erosion
2 transportation
3 deposition.

Impacts

a Explain how coastal erosion is having an impacton the following:

1 people living in the worst affected areas
2 local councils
3 tourists.

b Coastal erosion is a major issue all over the world. Carry out your own research using the internet. You could start by looking at the information in www.heinemann.co.uk/hotlinks

Management

a For each of the following, describe the strategy. Explain how useful it is in managing coastal erosion.

1 sea walls
2 rock armour
3 groynes
4 beach nourishment
5 revetments.

b Some people believe that the best management strategy is to do nothing and let nature take its course. Do you agree with this? Explain your answer.

Locations

a Describe the location of the Holderness coast.

b Describe and explain why the Holderness coastline has suffered so much erosion over the centuries.

c Write a case study describing and explaining how the village of Mappleton was protected from the eroding sea.

Issues

a Scientists believe that when coastal erosion is reduced in one place (due to the introduction of management strategies), it can lead to more rapid erosion in other locations further down the coast. Using the Holderness coastline as an example, try to prove or disprove this assertion.

5

Urbanisation in Brazil

Many cities in less economically developed countries (LEDCs) are growing rapidly. This is a result of a natural increase in population and **urbanisation** – the movement of people from rural areas into cities. City planners and local authorities face enormous problems because of these trends. In Brazil, the problem is particularly acute as thousands of people move from the rural north-east into cities such as São Paulo, Rio de Janeiro and Recife. In this unit, you will be asked to consider the following questions:

• Why are people leaving rural areas?

• What is life like for the migrants when they arrive in the cities?

• How are the city authorities trying to cope with the problems?

You will then be asked to put forward an improvement scheme for Heliopolis, a large suburb of São Paulo that has been growing at a rapid rate in the last 50 years. Will you attempt to help the entire area? What kind of improvement scheme will you recommend?

Population growth and urbanisation in Brazil

Many LEDCs are faced with the problems associated with a rising population and an increasing number of people who want to live in urban areas. Brazil, the largest country in South America, has particularly difficult problems, as shown by the trends in **Source A**.

Notice the rapid rise in population in recent years. Look at the increasing proportion of people who live in urban areas.

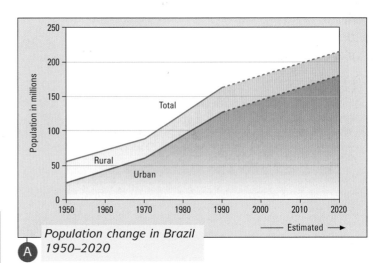

Population change in Brazil 1950–2020

A

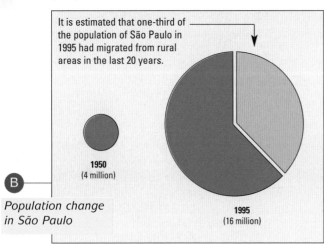

It is estimated that one-third of the population of São Paulo in 1995 had migrated from rural areas in the last 20 years.

1950
(4 million)

1995
(16 million)

B

Population change in São Paulo

Q

1 Compare these trends with population change in the UK.

2 How does São Paulo compare with London? Use a good atlas to find this information.

Activity

• Find out if São Paulo is typical of what is happening in other Brazilian cities.
• Do other LEDCs reflect the trends seen in Brazil?

Leaving the countryside

Much of the interior of north-east Brazil is sparsely populated. This rural area is one of the poorest regions in the world and over the last 50 years many thousands of people have migrated away. Most seek a new life in the south-eastern cities of Brazil, like São Paulo.

Life has always been difficult for the farmers who scratch a living from producing sugar cane. **Source D** is an extract from an article that sums up the struggle to survive. Most farmers do not own the land they work and landlords pay low wages, despite the harsh conditions. You can see why so many people want to leave.

North-east Brazil **C**

D *Life of a cane worker*

Poverty and despair

Try to imagine being born into a family of sugar cane workers in north-eastern Brazil. You would have about one chance in three of dying before your first birthday. If you are lucky enough to live one year, you would still face about one chance in six of dying before your fifth birthday. School? Fat chance. Even if there was a school you could attend, it would be decrepit and crowded. You would be hungry, dressed in rags and never have had your hands on a pencil or a book before you started school. For Brazil as a whole, only about one-fifth of the children who start primary school will finish, and the completion rate for plantation kids is even lower. By your early teen years you will be cutting cane.

On Sundays and some saints' days, you would put on your one decent set of clothing and walk an hour or two to the nearest market town to attend mass. That town, the plantation and the terrain in between are your entire world. By the age of 30 you would be toothless. By the age of 40, you would look like 60 and feel like 70. By the age of 50, your body would be wrapped in butcher paper, carried to the plantation burying ground in a borrowed coffin and dumped into a shallow grave.

Source: Human Society and the Global Economy, *K Taylor, 1996*

Drought on the land

Rainfall has always been low in the Ceará province of north-east Brazil. Much of the interior is Caatinga, a semi-desert. In recent years, the low rainfall has been particularly unreliable and a series of droughts has affected the region. The experiences of Rivaldo de Oliveira (see **Source E**) explain why people are leaving.

The last drop of rain I remember fell in November 1997. I used to grow enough manioc and corn to feed my family. It was always a struggle, but we got by. Now, we have to eat palma, a kind of cactus; it's the only thing that grows. We used to feed it to the cattle and our donkey. They have no use for it now, since they died last year.

We have to walk 10km to the nearest well. We collect water in tin cans. It's getting salty now.

We've had 15 children in all – eight have survived so far. The three eldest have already left for São Paulo and two more are going to join them next month. There's nothing here for them. I'm too old and tired to leave, but I may have to. I can't pay my rent and the landlord is threatening to throw me off the land. Where does he think I can get the money? It's hopeless.

I've joined the Movement for Landless Workers. Our Catholic priest encouraged me to do this. We are trying to persuade the government to help us, but so far nothing has happened. Last month, we walked to Juarzeirinho, and 50 of us occupied the Town Hall. Our protest ended when the police forced us out. They were brutal. My friend Jose was badly hurt.

 E *The views of a local farm worker*

Q
1 Why is it difficult for the local government in Ceara to help people like Rivaldo?
2 If all the young people leave for cities like São Paulo, what additional problems will people like Rivaldo face?

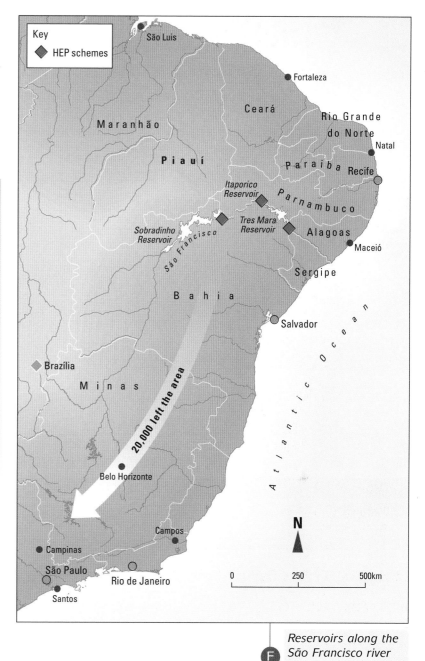
F *Reservoirs along the São Francisco river*

Forced off the land

In the last 50 years, the main river flowing through the north-east has been used to create hydroelectric power. Using money from the World Bank, three huge reservoirs have been created along the São Francisco River (see **Source F**). Some 120 000 people were displaced by the Sobradinho Project and 40 000 by the Itaporica Project. Those who owned land were compensated and resettled, but it was the most vulnerable who suffered the most. The landless became destitute overnight. They had three choices:

• Become totally dependent on charitable aid.
• Move to the interior and try to scratch out an existence in the Caatinga.
• Move out of the north-east region completely.

It is estimated that 20 000 have chosen the last option and moved to cities like São Paulo.

G *HEP plant*

53

Pushed and pulled into city life

Most of the migrants who leave regions like the north-east explain that their difficult life in the countryside was to blame. They can be said to be *pushed* away. Some are *pulled* to the cities because they are attracted by what they think the city has to offer.

| A | São Paulo – a city of many opportunities |

Push factors

Drought

Eviction

Low wages

No Education

The pull of São Paulo

I want to join my family

I'll get a job in the new factories

There is the chance of a regular wage

I'll send my children to school

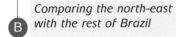

	North-east	Rest of Brazil
Life expectancy	52 (male) 58 (female)	59 (male) 64 (female)
Infant mortality	112/1000	57/1000
Adult literacy	51%	83%
% population below poverty line	49%	28%

| B | Comparing the north-east with the rest of Brazil |

Q.

1 What other measures of 'well being' could you use to compare the north-east with the rest of Brazil?

2 In addition to the PUSH and PULL factors given on the diagram, think of other things that would push you away from where you live or that would pull you towards a new place. Draw your own diagram and include them.

Arriving in the city – where to live?

After a long and difficult journey, migrants who arrive in cities like São Paulo are faced with the difficult task of finding somewhere to live and the need to search for a job. With little or no money, few skills and most important of all, no tenure (no right to be on the land), it is no surprise that many migrants are forced to set up home in a **favela** (the Brazilian name for a squatter settlement or shanty town). Most Brazilian cities have large areas where illegal settlers establish their first home. Compare the photographs in **Sources A** and **C**.

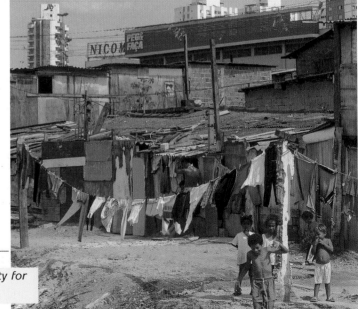

| C |

São Paulo – the reality for most migrants

São Paulo – simplified land use

São Paulo is Brazil's largest city.
It has a population of 9 million people (16 million within the São Paulo conurbation). It is still growing at a rapid rate. The maps in **Sources D** and **E** give you more information about São Paulo.

E

Sketch map to show the location of the favelas mentioned in the rest of this unit

Jardim Icarai

São Paulo City

Bras

Villa Mariana

Morumbi

Monte Azul

N

0   30km

Diadema

Santos

A t l a n t i c   O c e a n

D *A simplified land-use map of São Paulo*

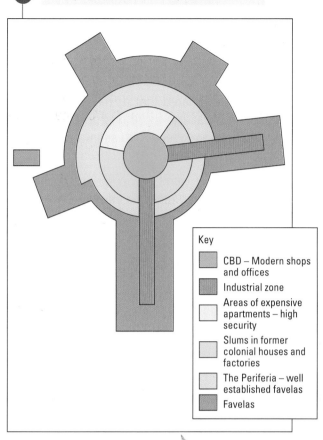

Key

▦	CBD – Modern shops and offices
▦	Industrial zone
▢	Areas of expensive apartments – high security
▢	Slums in former colonial houses and factories
▢	The Periferia – well established favelas
▦	Favelas

What are the favelas like?

They vary a great deal. Some of the long-established ones have improved over time – electricity, water and sewage pipes may have been added. Some of the building materials may have been improved – breeze blocks instead of cardboard! This section concentrates on the newest favelas – the areas where people would have to settle when they first arrive in São Paulo.

Typical sites

As the migrants have no legal right to land, nor any money to buy land, favelas are often built on land that nobody else has claimed. Examples include:

- Steep hillsides – landslides are a real danger after heavy rain.
- Marshland – a real problem because of disease linked to mosquitoes or the danger of flooding.

In addition to these sites, favelas are also built under motorway flyovers, on rubbish dumps, or adjacent to heavily polluted industrial areas.

F *Life in a favela*

Living conditions

- The houses – simple one-roomed shacks made out of scrap materials. They are crammed together as space is in short supply.
- Sanitation – no clean running water or sewer pipes. Streams flowing in and around the favela act as a water source and a convenient place to dispose of human waste.
- Disease – this spreads quickly, and diseases such as dysentery and typhoid are common. Infant mortality rates are high.
- Lack of security – crime rates are high. As the squatters have no right to be on the land, it is not uncommon for landlords to bulldoze the shacks.
- Employment – jobs are difficult to find. Wages are low and the journey to work can be a long one.
- Education – there are few formal schools, so literacy rates are low. Very young children are encouraged to earn money by street selling and shoe cleaning. Some beg in the CBD.

Activity

Write a report to the Catholic Charity Foundation describing the conditions you find in one of the new favelas. Say why the problems will be difficult to solve.

Favelas – improving the quality of life

The Chingapura Project, São Paulo

It is estimated that as many as three million people live in favelas like those described on the previous page. There are over 1 000 separate favelas in the metropolitan area of São Paulo.

In recent years, the authorities have made a determined effort to improve life for the residents of these areas. With more people arriving daily, the problem never goes away.

A co-ordinated approach to the entire city has been adopted; it is called the Chingapura Project. A huge amount of local authority money has been committed to the project, which has also been supplemented by additional funds from the Inter-American Development Bank (see **Source A**).

In the period 1995–2000 it is estimated that US $500 million has been spent tackling the problem.

In this section you will study a number of ways in which the city authorities have attempted to solve the problems of the favelas. Where would you start?

Inter-American Development Bank
Banco Interamericano de Desarrollo

• FOR IMMEDIATE RELEASE: 11 July 1996
• $150 m. to support favela scheme

WASHINGTON, DC – Paulo Maluf, mayor of the Brazilian city of São Paulo, and Enrique Iglesias, president of the IDB, today signed a $150 million loan contract for the upgrading of substandard housing in low income areas known as favelas. The loan is for a 25-year term (variable interest rates) and is supported by $100 million from local funds. Repayment begins in January 2000.

Press release from the inter-American Development Bank

No. of people in Morumbi favela:	55,000
No. of people re-housed:	33,000
No. of apartments constructed (5–11 storey flats):	9,000
Site fully serviced with:	water, sewage, waste disposal, electricity, street lighting
Rent:	range between $120 – $180 per month
Original landlord:	compensated for loss of land

Comprehensive Redevelopment programme in Morumbi, one of São Paulo's favelas

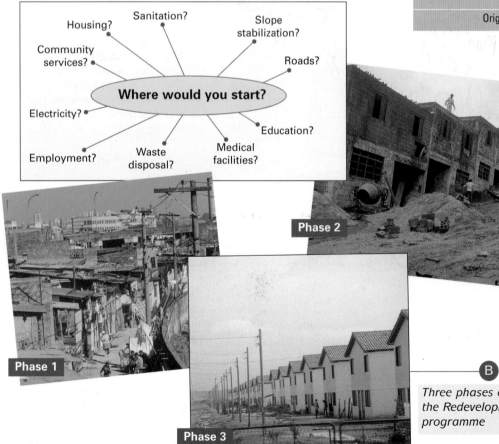

Phase 1

Phase 2

Phase 3

Three phases of the Redevelopment programme

• 'Most families in Morumbi can't afford the rent! Over the years many families have made improvements to their houses. Now their homes will be bulldozed and they will have to move away.'

• 'They were so concerned with the state of the houses, they've ignored our other needs. We want more jobs, schools and doctors.'

• 'It tackles all of the problems at once. The problem was so big, the only option was to knock it down and start again. People will have a legal right to be there.'

• 'Those in full-time work can afford the rent. It's very reasonable for what you get.'

Different opinions

Where would you start?

- Sanitation?
- Housing?
- Slope stabilization?
- Community services?
- Roads?
- Electricity?
- Education?
- Employment?
- Waste disposal?
- Medical facilities?

1 The comprehensive redevelopment programme

In 1996, it was decided to spend $150 million on a comprehensive redevelopment programme in the Morumbi district of São Paulo. This was, by far, the most ambitious scheme. The photographs in **Source B** show the three phases of the scheme.

Phase 1 Identify the district with the poorest living conditions

Phase 2 Bulldoze the site, forcing everyone to leave the area

Phase 3 Re-house 33,000 people (who can afford to pay rent)

Source C looks at the range of issues to be addressed and the numbers involved. Different opinions on the scheme are expressed in **Source D**.

2 The self-help scheme

In the Diadema favela, the authorities tried a different scheme. At a cost of $30 million, authorities were able to improve the quality of life for 80 000 people. Getting the locals to supply the labour saved money. The houses constructed were basic (see **Source E**), but functional. This self-help scheme involved a number of different phases.

By phasing this self-help scheme, disruption to the favela community was kept to a minimum. The project took nine years to complete, with 90 per cent of the original residents able to be re-housed. While the figures look impressive, there were winners and losers in the scheme. Rents start at $60 per month.

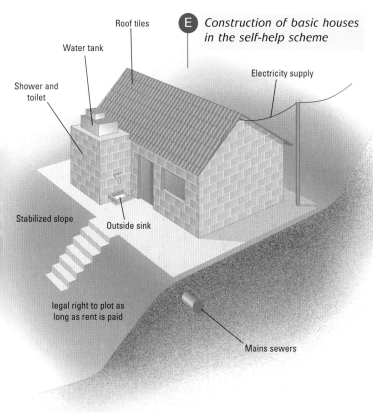

E *Construction of basic houses in the self-help scheme*

Roof tiles
Water tank
Shower and toilet
Electricity supply
Stabilized slope
Outside sink
legal right to plot as long as rent is paid
Mains sewers

 F *Winners and losers in the self-help scheme*

I'm so pleased with our new house. I know that it's not much to look at, but it's clean and my children can have a shower whenever they want. We all look after our homes – there's a real community spirit now. We know we won't get kicked off.

I'm one of the unlucky ones – I can't afford the rent because I haven't got a full-time job. They wouldn't let me stay. I had to move my family again. I've heard that I can have a plot in Jardim Icaraí, but I'm not sure what I'll find when I get there.

Activity

Discuss a sensible order for the following steps to be taken.

a Water and sewer pipes laid
b Residents given legal right to the land (tenure)
c Building materials supplied (breeze blocks, roof tiles, pipes, etc.)
d Favela zoned into sections for phased work
e Clearance of existing slum houses
f Slopes stabilised by terracing
g Supervisor appointed
h Security guards employed to reduce theft
i Residents construct basic houses

Q

1 Refer to scheme 1.
   a How has the $150 million been spent?
   b What kind of opposition is there to the scheme?
   c What kind of work is involved in this kind of scheme and who needs to be hired?

2 Refer to scheme 2.
   a Does the self-help scheme tackle all the problems of the favela? Who gains? Who loses?
   b Why can it be said that the problem has simply been moved?
   c What proportion of the favela dwellers in Morumbi have been helped?

3 Site and service Schemes

The city authorities in São Paulo recognise that inward migration will continue for the foreseeable future. Consequently, some of the funds from the Chingapura Project have been given over to Site and Service Schemes.

Jardim Icarai, a suburb of São Paulo, has seen a recent influx of new migrants. The land on the northern edge of the city is largely undeveloped for housing because it is:

- over 45km from the city centre
- under a major flightpath
- adjacent to an industrial area
- a steeply undulating landscape where mudslides are common.

Despite these problems, new migrants have begun to settle. **Source G** shows how, with a relatively small outlay of funds, the city authorities can reduce the problems of sanitation and tenure that affect most favelas.

5 000 plots can be prepared at a cost of $25 000. This includes major slope stabilisation, construction of water and sewage treatment works and the preparation of each individual plot.

1 Plot clearly marked 15/30m. Legal tenure if rent paid
2 Concrete base
3 Concrete lined latrine linked to sewer
4 Fresh water stand pipe
5 Washing sink
6 Slope stabilized by terracing hillside

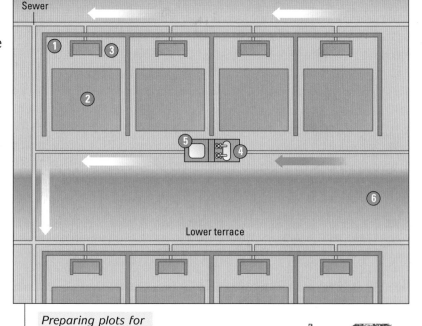

G Preparing plots for newcomers

4 Community-based projects

Many charitable organisations working in the favelas of São Paulo focus on helping community spirit. The Chingapura Project recognises the value of such work and has funded community-based projects.

In the favela of Monte Azul, $20 000 has been invested in a variety of schemes. These include:

- the creation of small workshops to enable waste products to be recycled (e.g. tyres into shoes).
- establishing day nurseries to provide basic education and allow both parents to seek work.

Monte Azul still has many problems, but the residents claim to have a better quality of life than some of their neighbours.

Collecting water from the Tiete, São Paulo's main river **H**

5 Sanitation Projects

In some of the more established favelas, such as Bras and Villa Mariana, charities such as CAFOD have helped to install basic sanitation schemes to reduce the constant problem of disease.

Funds from the Chingapura Project are now being directed to similar projects in other districts. It is estimated that $50 000 could reduce the risk of disease for as many as 200 000 residents of long established favelas.

Q 3 Refer to scheme 3.
   a Is the site and service scheme cost effective in the long run?
   b Will it encourage more migrants into the city?
   c If a favela is established around the scheme, what are the inevitable problems which will arise?

   4 Refer to scheme 4.
   a Why do residents of Monte Azul claim to have a better quality of life than their neighbours?

Your decision

Despite the huge input of funds through the Chingapura Project, thousands of people live miserable lives in the favelas untouched by redevelopment and improvement schemes. You have even seen people disadvantaged by existing improvement schemes. The cluster of favelas in the district of Heliopolis, to the north-east of São Paulo's CBD, still wait for significant funds to improve the lives of the residents.

Additional loans have just been agreed between the International Development Bank and the São Paulo City Authority. A further $50 million will be spent over the next five years. Where will the money be spent? What kind of projects will be recommended?

In this problem-solving exercise, we want *your* views. The city recognises the need to invest in Heliopolis, and here are some important facts to help shape your views.

A A simplified map of Heliopolis

B Socio-economic data from Heliopolis

Area within Heliopolis (see map A)	Characteristics	% of houses with		% unemployed	Life expectancy	Infant mortality	Adult literacy	% below poverty line
		access to safe water	legal access to electricity					
A Established 30 yrs +	Many charities active. Schools, clinics and community centres set up.	70	70	14	55 (m) 62 (f)	60/1000	80%	14%
B Developed 1985+	Occasional severe flooding. Current crime wave linked to drug problems.	40	20	20	49 (m) 54 (f)	100/1000	50%	35%
C Developed 2000+	New migrants, homes are very basic. Serious land-slide problems.	10	4	35	42 (m) 45 (f)	150/1000	50%	52%

The steep hillsides of Heliopolis

C

Q Compare the life expectancy, infant mortality, adult literacy and percentage of population below the poverty line data in **Source B** with **Source B** page 54.

D News articles

MUDSLIDE KILLS 20 IN SÃO PAULO

Mudslides caused by four days of torrential rain swept hundreds of makeshift homes down steep hillsides in an area of São Paulo called Heliopolis.

1 August 2000

10 August 2000

TEN KILLED IN DRUG WAR

Clashes between rival gangs were responsible for the death of ten young people. It is believed that drug trading, generated by chronic unemployment, is the root cause of the current feud.

Review exercise

Helpful hints before you begin

You have been asked by the city authorities to write a report to help them decide how to spend $50 million. Should the improvements schemes be:

- concentrated in one part of Heliopolis or spread across the three distinct zones within Heliopolis?

- in the style of a comprehensive redevelopment scheme, a number of self-help schemes, site and service schemes or community projects?

Hints

When you are asked to write a report like this, it is often difficult to know where to start. The advice on this page is directed at this particular task, but you can easily transfer the ideas to other reports where your teacher is asking for *your views*. You should give your views, but it is essential to explain *why* you hold those views. The kind of phrases your teacher likes to read include:

- When I studied ..., I noticed...
- The most important point is ... because ...
- One possible weakness in my plan is ... because ...

Using phrases like this means that you are explaining *why* you hold a viewpoint – you are getting to the heart of the matter. To get you started on this particular task, the points given on this page will give you a framework for your writing.

Always look at the task carefully!

Exactly what does your teacher want you to do? In this case, notice that the task is actually two tasks in one! Although the topic is the same, recognise that you need to give your opinion on two separate things. Always focus on one section at a time, otherwise your explanation can be very confusing to read.

Your report

1 Which area of Heliopolis should gain from an improvement scheme?

2 What kind of improvement scheme would you recommend from those tried before?

Really good answers bring together both parts at the end, when an integrated plan is discussed.

Hints

For 'which area' questions, structure answers like this:

- I think that the improvement scheme should be focused on area ..., because ...
- The main benefit of focusing on area ... is that ...
- I realise that the residents of area ... will not be happy, but I plan to ... which will mean ...
- * It is clear from map ... that ...; this is why I decided to ...
- * The news report on page ... suggested that ..., this is why I think ... is necessary.

For 'what kind of scheme' questions, structure your answer like this:

- I would spend most of the bank loan on a ... scheme because ...

  By doing ..., you will get immediate results because ...; I feel that ... is a longer term ...

  When I studied ..., it was clear to me that ...; I wouldn't want to make the same ...

- * When I looked at table ..., I could see that ...; my selected scheme will now mean ...
- * The information on page ... about the ... scheme, made me realise that ... is required.

Discuss with your teacher why phrases like these help you *justify* your ideas. The suggestions with the * **symbol** show that you are using the resources supplied. This is a good tactic to help you to get good marks.

Review exercise

Working in groups of four, take one of the following questions and prepare a brief report to summarise the main points.

1 Why are people leaving the north-east of Brazil?

2 What is life like for the migrants when they first arrive in São Paulo?

3 How are the city authorities trying to help?

4 Can every scheme be said to be successful?

Hints

Visual aids to support your presentation would be helpful.

Consider the same four questions for a similar issue from elsewhere in the world, such as India, Nigeria, or the Philippines.

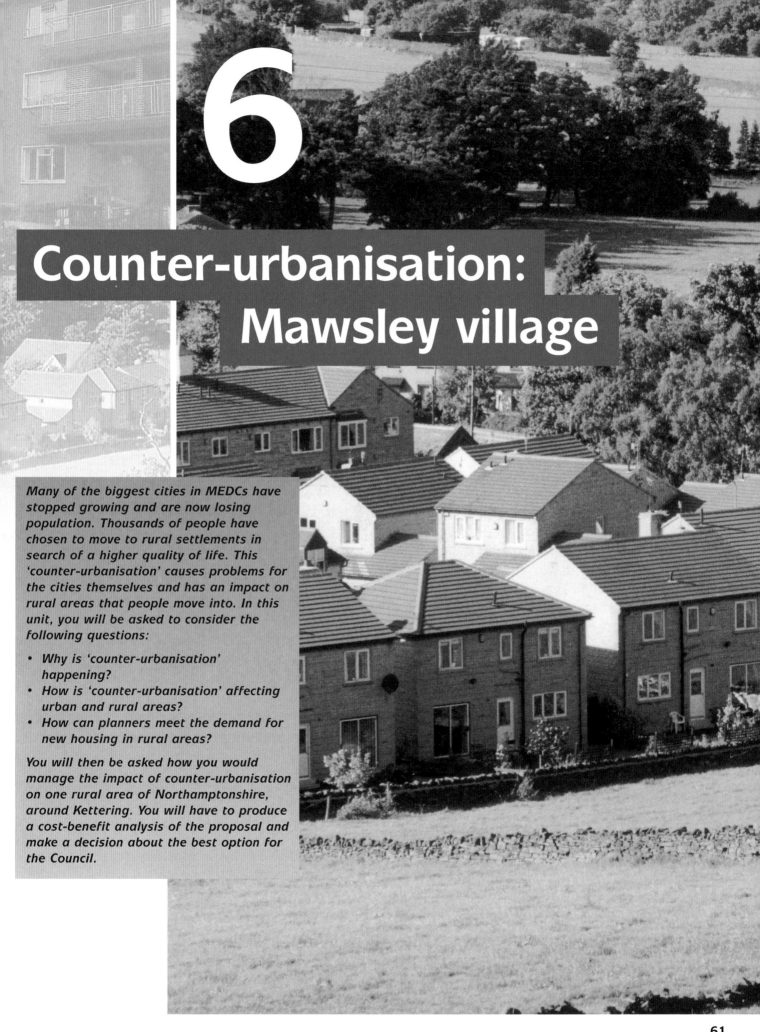

6

Counter-urbanisation: Mawsley village

Many of the biggest cities in MEDCs have stopped growing and are now losing population. Thousands of people have chosen to move to rural settlements in search of a higher quality of life. This 'counter-urbanisation' causes problems for the cities themselves and has an impact on rural areas that people move into. In this unit, you will be asked to consider the following questions:

- Why is 'counter-urbanisation' happening?
- How is 'counter-urbanisation' affecting urban and rural areas?
- How can planners meet the demand for new housing in rural areas?

You will then be asked how you would manage the impact of counter-urbanisation on one rural area of Northamptonshire, around Kettering. You will have to produce a cost-benefit analysis of the proposal and make a decision about the best option for the Council.

What is counter-urbanisation?

More Economically Developed Countries (MEDCs) have different urban problems from LEDCs. **Source A** shows the trends in urban and rural population in the UK over the last 50 years and beyond. The migration of people from urban to rural areas is called **counter-urbanisation**, and the graph shows that the trends are expected to continue. At first, people moved out of inner city areas, and housing expanded in the **suburbs** as big cities began to **sprawl** outwards. People could also move to **new towns** such as Milton Keynes, but – more recently – there has been demand for housing in smaller towns and villages away from the bigger cities.

There are a number of reasons why big cities are declining and why smaller settlements in rural areas are increasing. People move house for many different reasons, but there are common social, economic and environmental factors that push people to migrate from large **conurbations**.

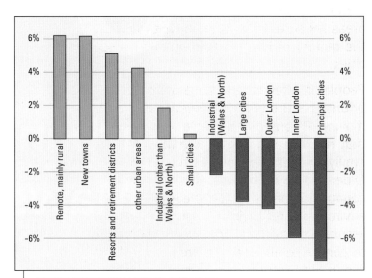

A *Population changes in Britain 1961–2001*

Q Why is the urban population declining in the UK?

B *The 'push' from conurbations*

Poorer quality housing
7.5 per cent of all housing is 'below a standard fit for human habitation', and most of this is in inner city areas

Pollution

Crime

Congestion

Noise

The 'push' from conurbations

Higher unemployment

Why are rural areas now so attractive?

People are often attracted to live in rural areas because, in some important respects, the **quality of life** is better than it is in big cities.

People of different ages have different priorities and therefore different reasons for moving. Parents, for example, might think that rural areas are safer to bring up a family, or that they have better schools. Older people might think that the countryside offers a more pleasant environment for their retirement or better leisure opportunities. However, it is possible to generalise about why more people now live in rural settlements, and why certain groups of people move house.

People now have much more choice about where to live. Since 1950, a number of developments have made it easier for people to move out of big cities:

- Services (such as shops) and employment have relocated away from city centres.
- Car ownership has increased.
- Road infrastructure has improved.
- Many new businesses have set up in rural locations.
- Disposable incomes have risen.

So people can live in one place and work in another. Millions of people in the UK now commute to work. They can live outside big cities, but can drive to the city to work, to shop and for entertainment and leisure.

Q Why do more people now live in rural areas?

A *The 'pull' of the countryside*

Lower crime rates

Quiet and peaceful

Better housing

Clean environment

BANK

Leisure opportunities

Uncrowded roads

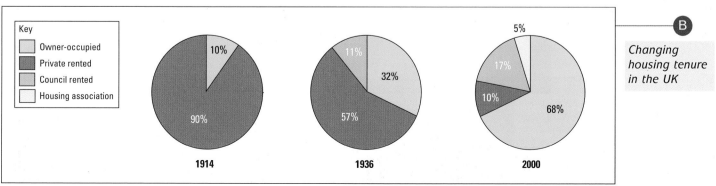

B *Changing housing tenure in the UK*

Key
- Owner-occupied
- Private rented
- Council rented
- Housing association

1914 — 10%, 90%

1936 — 11%, 32%, 57%

2000 — 5%, 17%, 10%, 68%

How does counter-urbanisation affect cities?

Counter-urbanisation causes problems for the cities themselves, and puts pressure on villages and the countryside.

When thousands of people move out of the inner city, it has a 'knock on' effect for other people:

• local shops and services
• local employers and businesses
• home owners
• the local council.

Source A shows some of these effects as a flow diagram. Everyone in this diagram loses money as a result of people moving away. House prices fall, businesses lose some of their best workers, there is less money for shops, and the local council gets less money to spend on essential services, such as council housing and schools. The local area declines and more people decide to move out. This is called a **vicious circle**. Four 'vicious circles' are shown in the diagram.

The lack of money in the urban economy will affect people's incomes, but it will also have an effect on the quality of the urban environment. **Source B** shows some of the effects of **urban decay**.

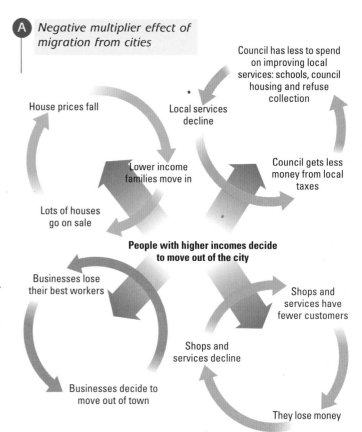

A *Negative multiplier effect of migration from cities*

Council has less to spend on improving local services: schools, council housing and refuse collection

Local services decline

House prices fall

Lower income families move in

Council gets less money from local taxes

Lots of houses go on sale

People with higher incomes decide to move out of the city

Businesses lose their best workers

Shops and services have fewer customers

Shops and services decline

Businesses decide to move out of town

They lose money

Q Describe and explain the social and economic effects of counter-urbanisation on the urban environment.

B

Urban decay and the impact on the environment

...and the countryside?

Many people who move out of cities want to buy detached houses. **Source A** shows the demand for new houses in England. There is most pressure for new housing in the south-east region particularly around London, but many counties in the Midlands and the south are under pressure from counter-urbanisation. People's desire to move to rural areas increases the demand for homes in these places. Thousands of new houses have to be built every year.

Northamptonshire is one of the counties under pressure to build new housing. The county is shown in **Source B**. Transport developments have boosted the economy in the Northamptonshire. Population growth has been above the national average and thousands of people have migrated into Northamptonshire over the last 40 years. Within the county itself, the towns have had to grow, but the main trend has been for people to move from the main towns into villages.

> **Q** Why are some parts of the country under more pressure than others?

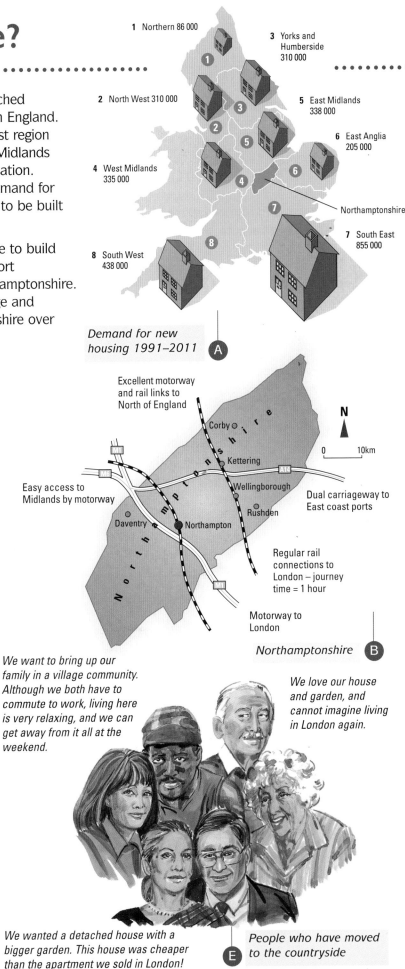

1 Northern 86 000
2 North West 310 000
3 Yorks and Humberside 310 000
4 West Midlands 335 000
5 East Midlands 338 000
6 East Anglia 205 000
7 South East 855 000
8 South West 438 000

Northamptonshire

Demand for new housing 1991–2011 **A**

Excellent motorway and rail links to North of England

Corby
Kettering
Wellingborough
Rushden
Daventry
Northampton

Easy access to Midlands by motorway

Dual carriageway to East coast ports

Regular rail connections to London – journey time = 1 hour

Motorway to London

Northamptonshire **B**

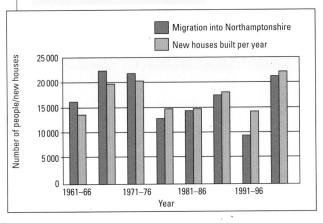

C *Northamptonshire: newcomers and new houses 1961–2001*

Key:
- Migration into Northamptonshire
- New houses built per year

(y-axis: Number of people/new houses, 0 to 25 000)
(x-axis: Year — 1961–66, 1971–76, 1981–86, 1991–96)

D *Population change in Northamptonshire compared with England and Wales*

Key
- Northamptonshire
- England and Wales

(y-axis: % population growth, 0 to 10)
(x-axis: Years — 1970, 1975, 1980, 1985, 1990, 1995)

We want to bring up our family in a village community. Although we both have to commute to work, living here is very relaxing, and we can get away from it all at the weekend.

We love our house and garden, and cannot imagine living in London again.

We wanted a detached house with a bigger garden. This house was cheaper than the apartment we sold in London!

People who have moved **E** *to the countryside*

Housing demands in Kettering

Kettering is one of the main towns in Northamptonshire. There is such demand for housing that 8 000 new houses must be built around the town between 1996 and 2016. The Council wants to allow 5 500 of the houses to be built in the town itself, and just 2 500 in the rural area around Kettering. **Source B** shows some of the developments that have been completed, with some proposed developments. The suburbs of Kettering have started to sprawl.

Kettering Borough Council has four aims for its new housing developments:

1 *to provide enough housing to meet demand*

2 *to provide housing that is the right type, tenure and size*

3 *to provide housing that is affordable*

4 *to minimise the impact of the new houses on local people and the environment.*

Q What sort of developments have taken place?

B *New developments in Kettering*

Aims for developments **A**

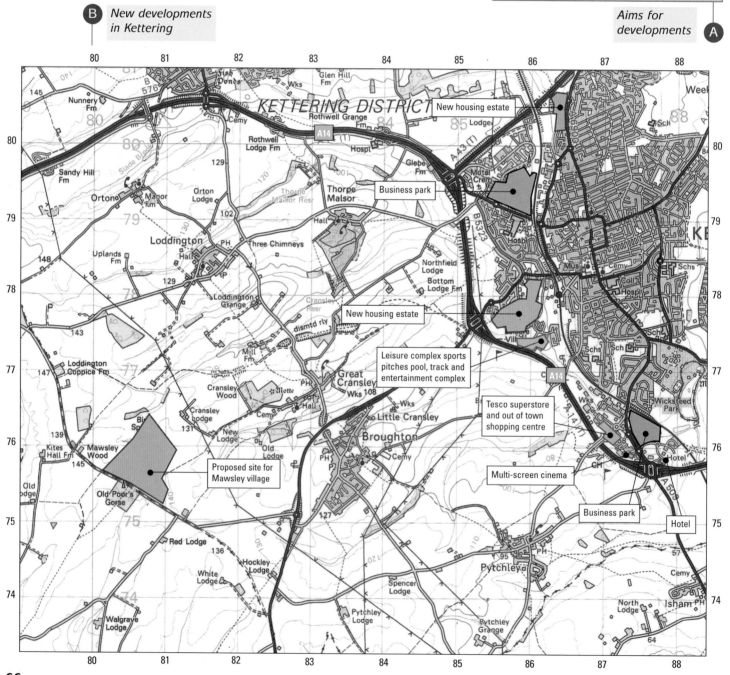

What options does the Council have?

Whenever a new plan is proposed, Kettering Council draws up a **cost-benefit analysis** of the proposal. It looks at all the advantages of the plan ('benefits') and works out all the disadvantages that it will cause ('costs'). This is not easy to do, because some benefits are also problems:

• A benefit for one person might be a problem for someone else.
• Something that benefits the environment might be an economic problem for local business.

Activity

Put the information from **Source C** into a spreadsheet and then decide what type of graph would be best to show each of the three sets of information. Explain why you chose that graph.

C

Survey of people wanting to move to the area

What type of house do you want?	
Property type	% of responses
flat/apartment	6
terraced	5
semi-detached	22
detached	67

What size house do you want?	
No. of bedrooms	% of responses
1–2 bedrooms	13
3 bedrooms	39
4 bedrooms	35.5
5 bedrooms	12.5

What housing tenure do you want?	
Type of tenure	% of responses
owner occupied	85
housing to rent	15

Plan A: Concentrate all development in the town
• Build all 8 000 new houses within the town of Kettering

Plan B: Develop small villages
• 5 500 new houses in Kettering
• 2 500 new houses in the 25 local villages

Plan C: Build new village at Mawsley
• 5 500 new houses in Kettering
• 1 750 new houses in local villages
• 750 new houses in a new village (Mawsley)

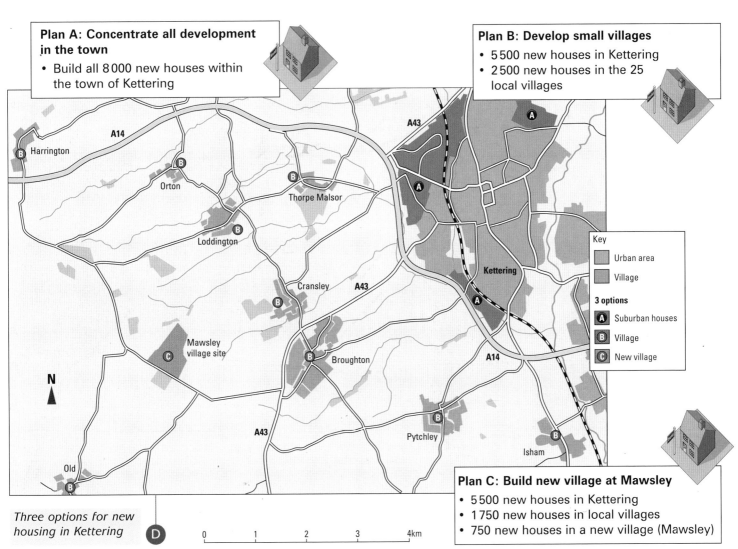

Three options for new housing in Kettering **D**

Key
- Urban area
- Village

3 options
- **A** Suburban houses
- **B** Village
- **C** New village

What 'benefits' will Mawsley village bring?

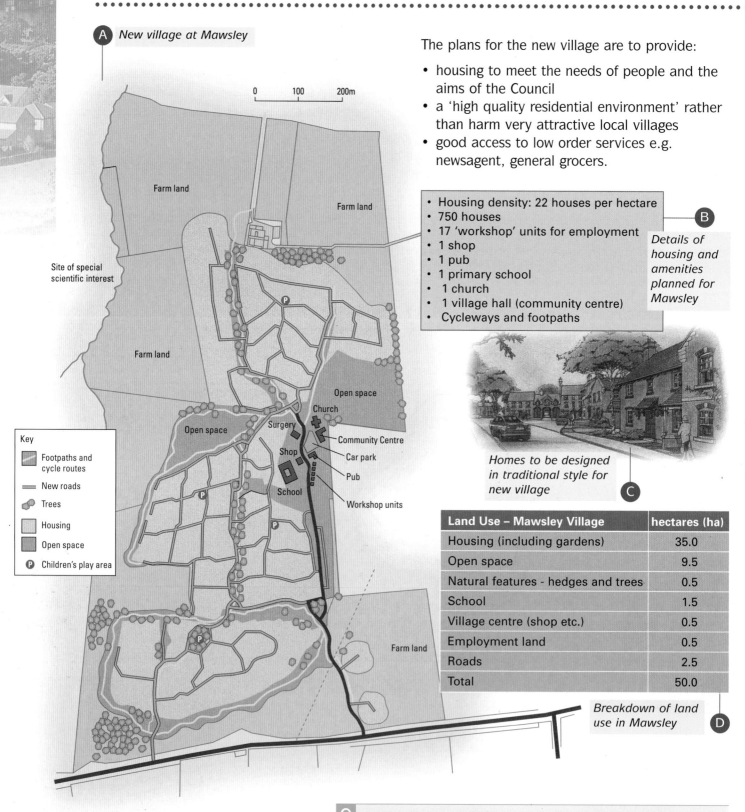

A *New village at Mawsley*

0   100   200m

Farm land

Farm land

Site of special scientific interest

Farm land

Open space

Open space

Church

Surgery

Community Centre

Shop

Car park

Pub

School

Workshop units

Farm land

Key
- Footpaths and cycle routes
- New roads
- Trees
- Housing
- Open space
- **P** Children's play area

The plans for the new village are to provide:

- housing to meet the needs of people and the aims of the Council
- a 'high quality residential environment' rather than harm very attractive local villages
- good access to low order services e.g. newsagent, general grocers.

B *Details of housing and amenities planned for Mawsley*

- Housing density: 22 houses per hectare
- 750 houses
- 17 'workshop' units for employment
- 1 shop
- 1 pub
- 1 primary school
- 1 church
- 1 village hall (community centre)
- Cycleways and footpaths

Homes to be designed in traditional style for new village **C**

Land Use – Mawsley Village	hectares (ha)
Housing (including gardens)	35.0
Open space	9.5
Natural features - hedges and trees	0.5
School	1.5
Village centre (shop etc.)	0.5
Employment land	0.5
Roads	2.5
Total	50.0

Breakdown of land use in Mawsley **D**

Q Describe the 'quality of life' that this new village would provide for its residents, using these headings:
- housing
- environment
- access to services.

What will be the 'costs' of the new village?

The new village will have an impact on the environment. The resulting pollution can take different forms:

• *Air* pollution from gas emissions can affect vegetation and wildlife habitats, as well as local people
• *Water* pollution, from liquids, gets into the water cycle and affects ecosystems as well as people
• *Noise* pollution can affect both people and wildlife
• *Visual* pollution affects people when a development is an 'eyesore'.

The effects can be worse when the construction work is being done, but there will be different impacts once the new village is built.

There will be an impact on wildlife in the area. The planned site for the village centre is 300m away from the SSSI, which is a habitat to rare birds such as barn owls and snipes as well as rare plants and animals such as badgers and foxes.

Q
1 What will be the impact of increased traffic flows?

2 Is it better to concentrate the impact in one place or to spread it around the smaller villages?

3 Do the 'benefits' of Mawsley outweigh the 'costs'?

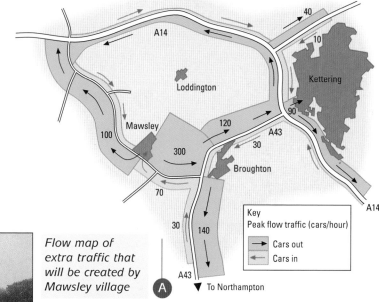

Flow map of extra traffic that will be created by Mawsley village

A

▼ To Northampton

Key
Peak flow traffic (cars/hour)
→ Cars out
← Cars in

Planned site for village

B

Impact on local people **D**

It's better to put all the new housing in one place rather than ruining 20 small villages.

Loddington resident

The A43 is already a busy and dangerous road.

Broughton resident

They're planning to build 750 new homes within 500m of an SSSI. It can really damage wildlife habitats.

Cransley resident

C

Visual impact

Is Plan B any better?

Loddington is a local village that is under pressure from new housing developments. **Source A** shows the traditional character of the housing in Loddington. Any new housing will have an effect on the old village. Some of the effects will be 'good' for the village, but some will be 'bad'.

> **Q** What will be the impact of extra houses in the local villages? Use these headings for your answer:
> - land use
> - services
> - traffic
> - the environment.

The effects on a village community are difficult to predict. There is often some hostility when new people move into a village community.

Activity

1 Calculate the percentage of land use per activity in the village of Loddington, and compare your findings with the village of Mawsley (see **Source A**, page 68).

2 Discuss how 200 new houses will affect the land use in Loddington.

3 Imagine that you live in Loddington and developers have asked for permission to build 100 new houses in your village. Write a letter to the local newspaper explaining what you think about the plan. You must be persuasive in your argument.

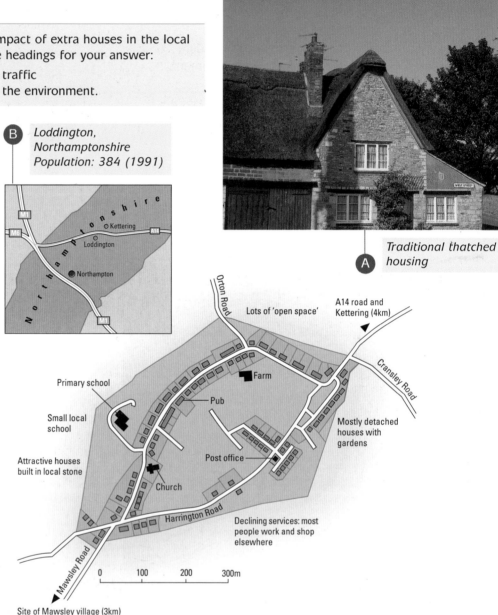

A Traditional thatched housing

B Loddington, Northamptonshire
Population: 384 (1991)

Primary school

Small local school

Attractive houses built in local stone

Church

Farm

Pub

Post office

Lots of 'open space'

A14 road and Kettering (4km)

Mostly detached houses with gardens

Declining services: most people work and shop elsewhere

Orton Road

Cransley Road

Harrington Road

Mawsley Road

0   100   200   300m

Site of Mawsley village (3km)

Review point

Decide what is the best way to meet the need for new houses in the Kettering area. Present your report to Kettering Council in three parts:

1 The best solution to the problem of housing provision: to build in Kettering, to build a new village, or to expand existing villages

2 Reasons why this is the best solution.

3 Recommendations that would minimise the impact of new developments on
- local people
- the local environment.

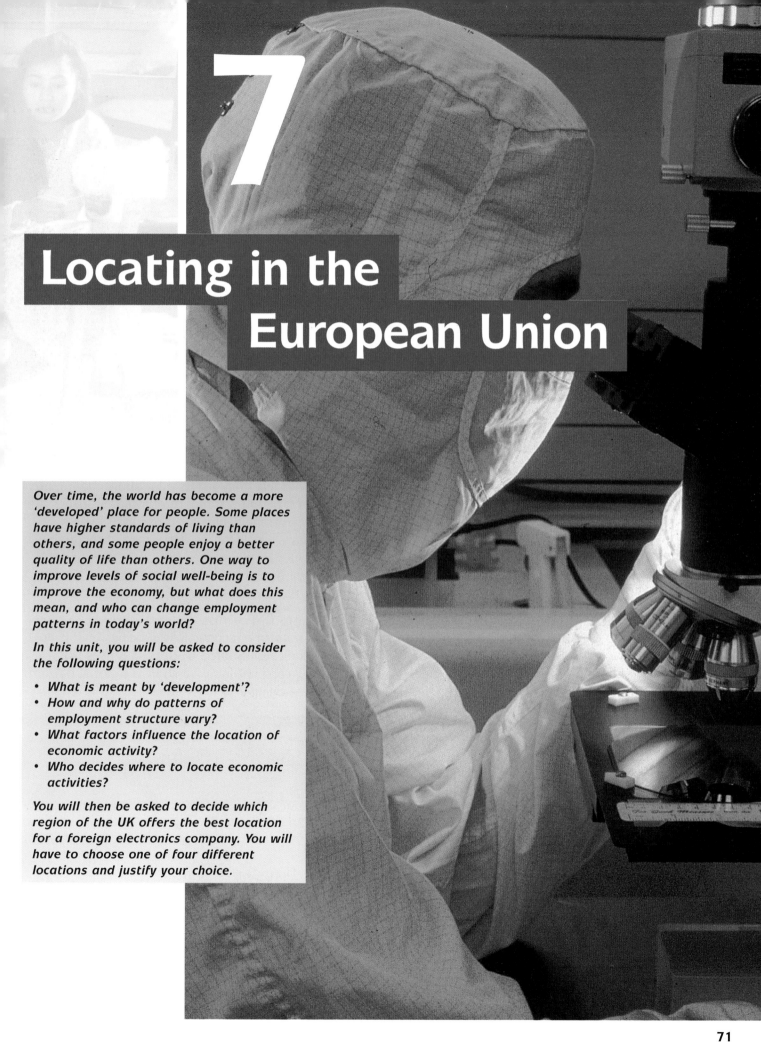

7

Locating in the European Union

Over time, the world has become a more 'developed' place for people. Some places have higher standards of living than others, and some people enjoy a better quality of life than others. One way to improve levels of social well-being is to improve the economy, but what does this mean, and who can change employment patterns in today's world?

In this unit, you will be asked to consider the following questions:

• What is meant by 'development'?
• How and why do patterns of employment structure vary?
• What factors influence the location of economic activity?
• Who decides where to locate economic activities?

You will then be asked to decide which region of the UK offers the best location for a foreign electronics company. You will have to choose one of four different locations and justify your choice.

What is meant by 'development'?

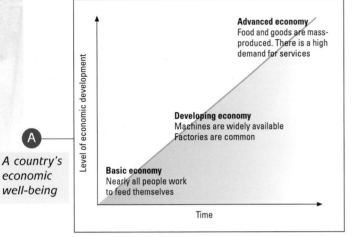

A country's economic well-being

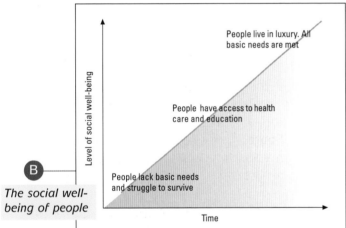

The social well-being of people

Development means different things to different people. It can mean the 'economic development' of a place, or it can refer to the 'social development' of people.

- 'Economic well-being' looks at the economic development of a place, rather than the people who live there. **Source A** shows that a country's economy should start at a low level and then become more advanced over time.

- 'Social well-being' looks at people and measures their standard of living. **Source B** shows how this improves over time. However, it is not always this simple and if a region suffers bad times, then people's quality of life can become worse.

Geographers use dozens of different indicators to measure levels of development. Some indicators just measure one aspect of a country, but some indicators are better because they tell us a lot about the economy and people's standard of living. Statistics are usually just average figures for a region or even a whole country, which can be misleading. If the average life expectancy for a nation is 50 years, then half the people might live to over 90 and the poorest 50 per cent might die under the age of 10.

Source C uses GNP (Gross National Product) to show the global pattern of economic well-being. GNP is an economic indicator. **Source D**, opposite, uses the Human Development Index to show the global pattern of social well-being.

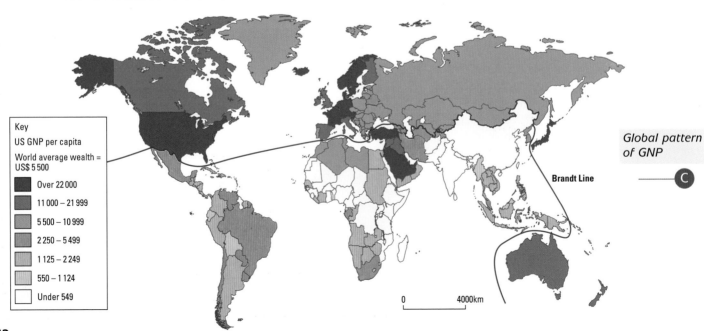

Global pattern of GNP

Key

US GNP per capita

World average wealth = US$ 5 500

	Over 22 000
	11 000 – 21 999
	5 500 – 10 999
	2 250 – 5 499
	1 125 – 2 249
	550 – 1 124
	Under 549

C

Brandt Line

0   4000km

D *The Human Development Index*

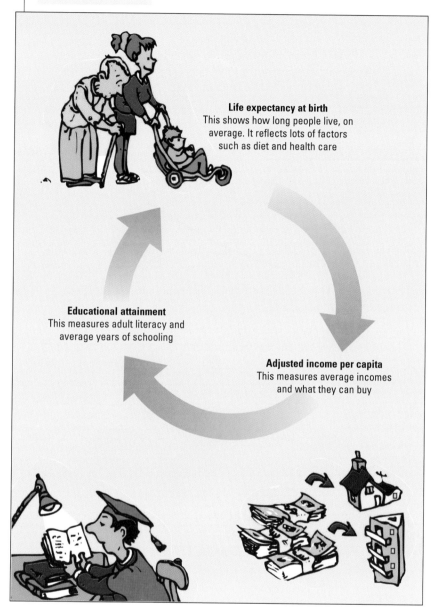

Life expectancy at birth
This shows how long people live, on average. It reflects lots of factors such as diet and health care

Educational attainment
This measures adult literacy and average years of schooling

Adjusted income per capita
This measures average incomes and what they can buy

Geographers use economic and social indicators to divide the world into rich and poor. The Brandt Line splits the world into the richer 'North' and the poorer 'South'. This line was first drawn in 1980 and it is still used to divide the world into MEDCs (more economically developed countries) and LEDCs (less economically developed countries). Geographers do not agree about the best way to map 'development'.

The Human Development Index obviously tells us a lot about a country. People will live longer, on average, if they have a good diet, good health care and a comfortable quality of life. This suggests that a country's economy is also well developed, so that people are not overworked in poor conditions and on low wages.

GNP tells us how much money is being generated through the economy. If lots of people simply grow food for their own family, then this does not count towards a country's GNP. A country that manufactures lots of products and makes money overseas will have high GNP.

Countries that are economically wealthy usually have high levels of social well-being too, although this is not always the case. **Source E** is a scattergraph that shows the relationship between GNP and life expectancy.

E *Scattergraph of GNP and life expectancy*

Q 1 Are some indicators more useful than others?

2 Can the world be divided into MEDCs and LEDCs with one line?

3 What are the advantages and disadvantages of this division?

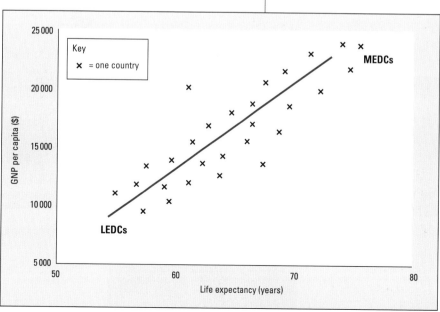

How do patterns of employment structure vary?

What happens over time?

As the economy of a country develops over time, so there is a shift in employment. **Source A** shows these changes:

- Numbers employed in the primary sector decline steadily.
- Numbers employed in tertiary jobs increase steadily.
- Factory employment – the secondary sector – increases at first, before numbers decrease.

An LEDC, like India, has a much higher percentage of primary workers than an MEDC like the UK. The percentage employed in secondary and tertiary employment is also very different. **Source C** gives some clues to explain some of the differences between LEDCs and MEDCs.

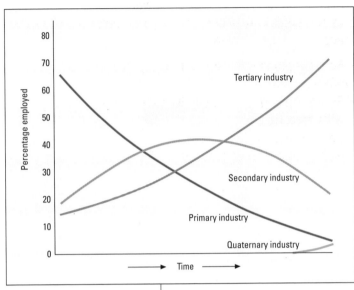

A Changing employment structure

Q Why does a country's employment structure change over time?

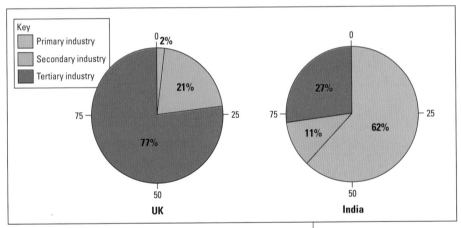

B Employment structure in the UK and India

C *Different kinds of work in India and the UK*

How does employment structure vary in the EU?

The EU is a geographical union of MEDCs, but even among these wealthy countries there are different levels of economic development and social well-being. **Source D** shows the pattern of employment structure within the EU and the areas that are eligible for economic help through development grants.

- Some regions still have lots of primary employment.
- Some regions are heavily industrialised with factories.
- Some parts of Europe have a very high proportion of tertiary workers.

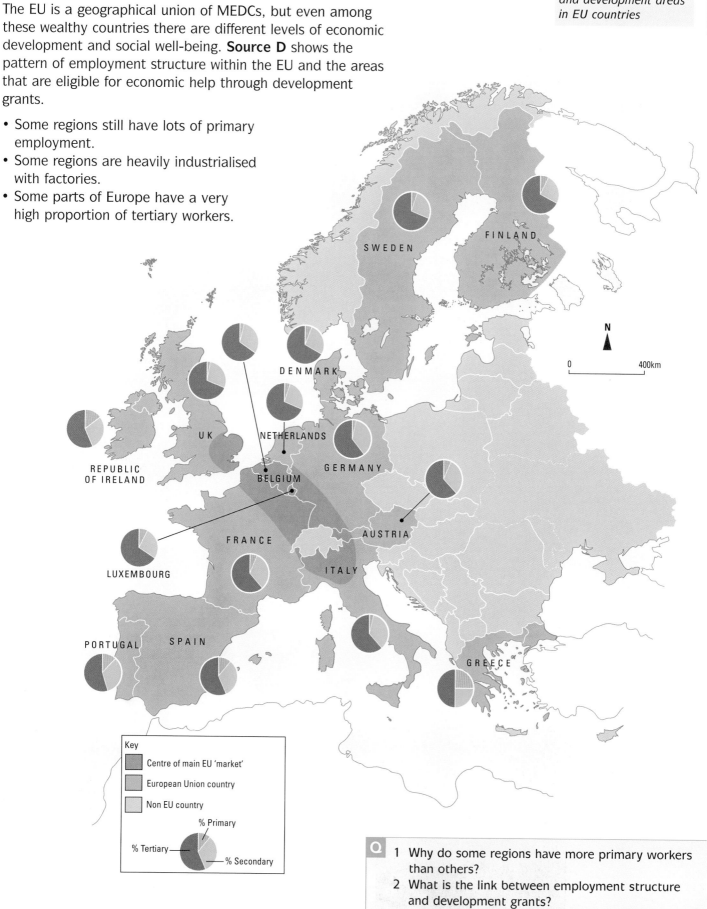

Key
- Centre of main EU 'market'
- European Union country
- Non EU country

% Primary
% Tertiary
% Secondary

What factors influence the location of economic activity?

To make money, businesses must keep their costs as low as possible. The location of an economic activity determines its costs and profits, so lots of factors must be considered, as **Source A** shows. Primary activities, like farming and mining, locate where physical factors are most suitable, but factories (secondary activities) and services (tertiary activities) are influenced by many different location factors. **Source B** shows how the importance of each factor will depend on the type of factory.

> **Q** How important are different location factors?

A *Location factors star diagram*

Land

- Size of site
- Rents
- Wage levels
- Transport infrastructure

Labour — **Location factors** — **Transport**

- Skills of workers
- Distance to raw materials/parts
- Size of market
- Closeness to market

Market

Our biggest cost is transporting raw materials because they are so bulky. We need a big site next to a deep water port.

Integrated steelworks

Textiles and clothing factories are labour-intensive. We need a huge workforce, so we must keep wage levels low.

Clothing factory

Transporting cars overseas is expensive, so we need to locate near big population centres. Lots of people means lots of sales.

Car assembly factory

High-tech industry

B What factors influence different economic activities?

We are 'footloose'. We can choose to locate almost anywhere because our transport costs are so low. Our research facilities need to be near a skilled workforce.

Who decides where to locate economic activities?

Big business can save millions by choosing the best location. For many companies the cheapest location is now in LEDCs, where costs are lower. Multinational companies (MNCs) such as Nike, Sony and Ford have plants in several countries. The directors of a company will decide where to locate their economic activity, but other people also have a role in decisions. Local people, the local council and even the national government can stop economic activities from locating in certain places, and they can attract business as well. The biggest MNCs are richer than many small countries, so they can generate thousands of extra jobs wherever they locate. This is called the 'multiplier effect'. Governments try to attract MNCs to locate in their country by offering:

- special grants and subsidies
- low rates of tax
- cheap sites with low rents.

The government of the European Union (EU) also attracts MNCs by charging import taxes on goods that are imported from other countries. **Source A** shows why some MNCs from places like Japan, Korea and the USA want to locate in the EU.

Q How can a government influence the location of economic activity?

A The EU trade system

SPECIAL GRANTS

FREE TRADE ZONE

LOW TAXES

CHEAP SITES

GOODS TO DECLARE

CHEAP LABOUR

Your decision

Top location

Every year hundreds of MNCs set up factories in EU countries in order to gain better access to European markets and avoid import taxes. Many locate in regions that offer special EU grants. This can a save a business millions of pounds each year.

Britain is Europe's top location for inward investment. getting over 25 per cent of all investment into the EU, including 40 per cent of all US and Japanese investment. With more than 18 000 foreign firms in the UK, they now account for one-fifth of all employment in the country and bring in billions of pounds in export earnings. Since 1997, foreign investment has created more than 90 000 new jobs in the UK and safeguarded 158 000 others.

Solving the problem: where is the best location?

KEC is a South Korean electronics firm that wants to expand its business in Europe by setting up a new factory in the UK. **Source B** gives important details about the company. **Source C** on the opposite page gives details of the four regions that you can choose.

You have been asked to choose the best location. The best sites will be the cheapest ones, but they must be accessible to the main business centres in the EU.

• Make a large copy of the table below.
• Use all the information and your own knowledge to fill in the table and give each location factor a score.

> 3 = excellent/attractive   1 = OK
> 2 = good   0 = bad/unattractive

• Add the totals to find the best location. There might then be other factors to consider, such as 'environment'.

• Justify your choice of location and explain why this location is better than the others.

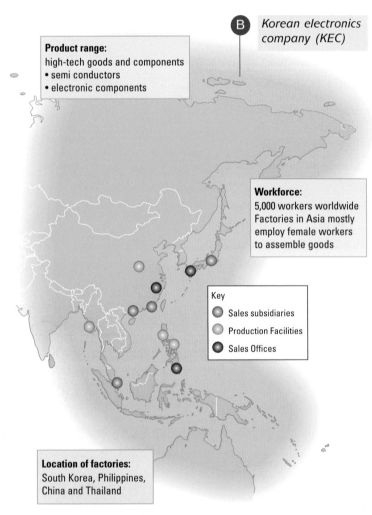

B *Korean electronics company (KEC)*

Product range:
high-tech goods and components
• semi conductors
• electronic components

Workforce:
5,000 workers worldwide
Factories in Asia mostly employ female workers to assemble goods

Key
• Sales subsidiaries
• Production Facilities
• Sales Offices

Location of factories:
South Korea, Philippines, China and Thailand

	Cornwall (SW) **scores**	Belfast (N Ireland) **scores**	Liverpool (NW) **scores**	Dover (SE) **scores**
Wage levels				
Factory rents				
Access to EU markets				
EU grants				
Other factors				
TOTAL				

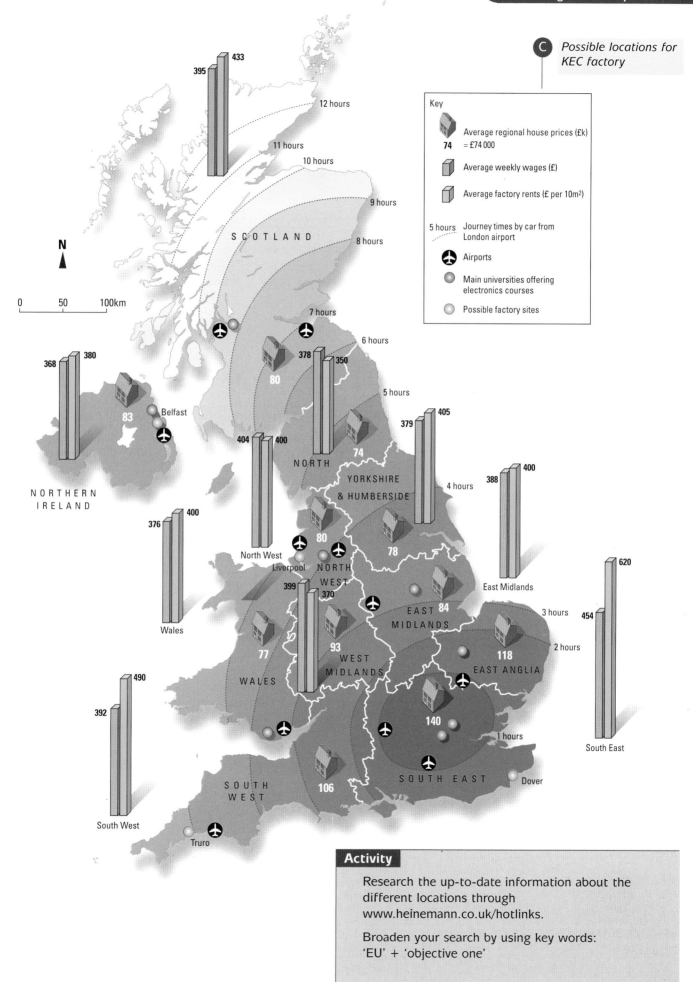

C Possible locations for KEC factory

Key

⌂ Average regional house prices (£k)
74 = £74 000

▯ Average weekly wages (£)

▯ Average factory rents (£ per 10m²)

5 hours ⋯ Journey times by car from London airport

✈ Airports

● Main universities offering electronics courses

○ Possible factory sites

395 433

SCOTLAND

12 hours
11 hours
10 hours
9 hours
8 hours
7 hours
6 hours
5 hours
4 hours
3 hours
2 hours
1 hours

N

0 50 100km

368 380

Belfast
83

NORTHERN IRELAND

378 350
80

NORTH
74

YORKSHIRE & HUMBERSIDE

379 405

388 400
East Midlands

404 400

376 400

NORTH WEST
North West
Liverpool
80
78

399 370
93

WEST MIDLANDS

EAST MIDLANDS
84

620

454

Wales

490

392

WALES
77

EAST ANGLIA
118

140

South East

SOUTH WEST
106

SOUTH EAST

Dover

South West

Truro

Activity

Research the up-to-date information about the different locations through www.heinemann.co.uk/hotlinks.

Broaden your search by using key words: 'EU' + 'objective one'

79

Review exercise

1 Here are six important terms from this unit. Write a definition for each one:

- economic development
- social well-being
- economic well-being
- GNP
- life expectancy
- employment structure.

2 Now find the six correct terms that match these definitions:

Activities like farming and mining that produce raw materials

P_ _ _ _ _ _

The service sector

T_ _ _ _ _ _ _

The economic union of European countries

E _

A factory that can locate almost anywhere

F_ _ _ _ _ _ _ _

A company which has bases in several different countries

M_ _

When a new development has the effect of bringing other jobs and developments to the local economy

M_ _ _ _ _ _ _ _ _   E_ _ _ _ _

3 Here are the important key ideas from this unit. Use these questions to revise the topic:

a) What is meant by development?
- Give one important difference between economic and social indicators (1)
- What is the Human Development Index? (1)

b) Why does employment structure vary?
- Give three reasons for the decline of primary employment over time (3)
- Give three reasons for the increase in tertiary employment (3)

c) What factors influence the location of economic activity?
- Give five location factors (5)
- Explain why a clothes factory and a car assembly factory locate in different places (4)
- Give two reasons why MNCs from outside the EU want to locate in the United Kingdom (2)

d) Who decides where to locate economic activity?
- Give three reasons why MNCs decide to locate in different countries (3)
- Give three different ways that governments can attract industry (3)

4 In conclusion: how can new industry improve a region's economic and social well-being? Use these words in your answer:

- GNP
- economic
- jobs
- wages
- multiplier effect
- services
- social
- quality of life
- standard of living.

8

Impact of economic activity on the environment

Case study: Tourism on the Norfolk Broads

Situated in Norfolk and north Suffolk, the Broads is an area of outstanding natural beauty and is Britain's finest wetland. It has a status similar to that of a National Park. The Broads Authority has been set up to conserve the natural beauty of the area while promoting the area for the enjoyment of people. This dual aim can easily lead to conflict.

The influx of thousands of visitors looking to enjoy this unique landscape has created a flourishing tourist industry. The **multiplier effect** means that the industry has become the main source of jobs and wealth creation in the region. Can the tourist industry be accused of changing, or even harming, the very landscape people have come to enjoy? Is conflict inevitable? The Broads Authority has a difficult task in striking a balance between exploitation and conservation. Problem solving is at the heart of their work. In this unit, you will be asked to consider the following questions:

• Why is the Broads so attractive to tourists?
• How much of the local economy is dependent on the tourist industry?
• How can the industry damage the environment?
• How can exploitation take place without harming the environment?

You will then be asked how you would develop a site to enhance the tourist facilities in Hoveton, in the heart of the Broads. Is exploitation possible without harming the local environment? Can conflicts be resolved?

The Broads – a special place

A *Location map of the Broads*

The Broads is Britain's finest wetland. It covers an area of 303km² and is located in the East Anglian counties of Norfolk and Suffolk.

Its rich wildlife and unique landscape attract 2 million visitors each year. In recent years, a thriving tourist industry has been established to provide for visitors wishing to stay for a week or two and for those on day trips.

The pleasures of the winding waterways, old villages, windpumps and grazing marshes can be enjoyed in many kinds of outdoor pursuits. Whether boating, birdwatching, fishing, walking or cycling, the potential for different forms of quiet recreation in the Broads is immense.

There are 200km of safe, navigable waterway with over 60 boatyards offering sailing or cruising holidays.

The huge potential for tourism   **B**

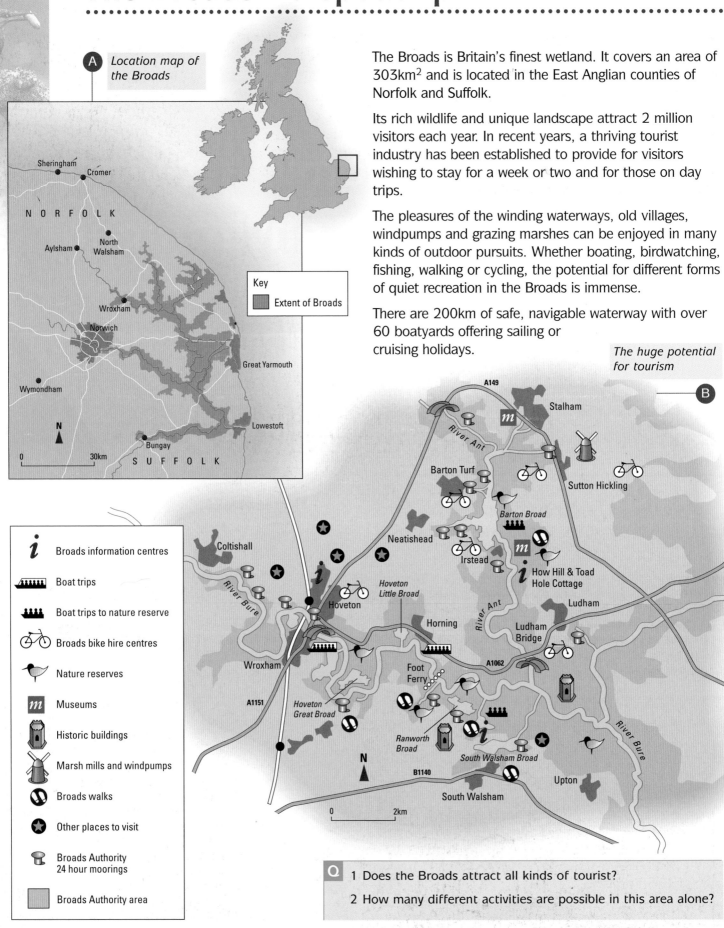

Key
Extent of Broads

i Broads information centres

Boat trips

Boat trips to nature reserve

Broads bike hire centres

Nature reserves

m Museums

Historic buildings

Marsh mills and windpumps

Broads walks

Other places to visit

Broads Authority 24 hour moorings

Broads Authority area

Q 1 Does the Broads attract all kinds of tourist?

2 How many different activities are possible in this area alone?

A special place – a natural landscape?

Within the area of the Broads, there is a huge variety of **habitats** and **landscape types** – rivers, open water, fens, carr woodland and drained marshland, all of which are linked to form one integral wetland.

This is not a natural landscape – it was created by peat digging over 700 years ago. Peat was once the principal source of fuel in Norfolk. Turves of peat were cut from pits which, over the course of time, began to fill with water and were abandoned. It was over a 700-year period that this landscape began to evolve. Today, it is a mecca for those interested in fauna and flora. When left undisturbed, the varied ecosystems support a huge range of animals and plants.

A *A kingfisher – just one example of birdlife on the Broads*

B

Flora and fauna of the Broads

Key
1 Bewick swan
2 Heron
3 Bittern
4 Grass snake
5 Marsh Harrier

D *Wildlife conservation in action*

Q Visiting landscapes like the Broads may only appeal to a minority. Should areas like this be protected?

Activity

1 Carry out research into a marsh ecosystem. Construct a food-web to show the inter-relationship between the producers and consumers.
2 Discuss why the marsh fen ecosystem can be said to be fragile.

C

The natural landscape of the Broads

Fen restored to bring back the bittern

Many people will have spotted the bittern in books, but very few will have ever seen it in the wild. A little smaller than a heron, its numbers have steadily declined from about 80 'booming' males in 1954 to less than 20 today. Of these, 16 are found at 8 sites in Norfolk and Suffolk.

The bittern lives among the reeds of wetland areas where it is camouflaged by its streaky brown plumage. It feeds on fish, particularly eels and small water animals.

The Broads Authority has undertaken 'Bittern Projects' to restore its habitat, with a view to increasing numbers.

Source: adapted from P. Heath, Broadcaster, 2000

More tourists – more attractions!

A *Norwich and Norfolk Tourist Agency brochure*

PENINSULA COTTAGES

BOOKINGS TO: Moore & Co, Staitheway Road
Wroxham, Norfolk NR12 8RN
Tel: 01603 783311 Fax: 01603 784295

🐚 ▦ 🚗 🛥 🏃 🔲 ∪ 🥢 ⸙ ❄ 🐴 GE ▣ ▢ ⊖ LF
📷 ✈ ⛰ 🔼

The Peninsula is situated on the southern side of the river on the famous Norfolk Broads at Wroxham, which is five miles from the ancient cathedral city of Norwich and within 20 minutes of the coast. The Peninsula is a unique collection of self-catering cottages, all of which have views of the water. There are one, two, three and four bedroom properties, all of which are luxuriously furnished to provide comfortable and relaxed living.

Those involved in the tourist industry have been quick to recognise the opportunities arising from the influx of thousands of visitors to this unique area.

The Broads can boast a wide range of attractions beyond the natural beauty of the area. Many of these are illustrated in **Sources A** and **B**.

Whatever the reason for visiting the area, the impact of tourism has been highly significant.

The graph in **Source C** shows current and estimated spending figures by tourists over a five-year period.

WATERSIDE TERRACE RESTAURANT & BAR

Hotel Wroxham, The Bridge, Wroxham NR12 8AJ
Tel: 01603 782061

Wroxham riverside dining! "The Waterfront Terrace" offers delicious home cooked food – bar snacks, daily carvery and full à la carte menu. Outdoor heated terrace and plenty of parking. Families most welcome!
Sunday lunch our speciality, two or three course menu from £8.95.
Opening Times: Winter 12noon–2.30pm (3pm Sun), 7–9pm.
Summer 12noon–9.30pm. Breakfast daily.

B *Eating out in the Broads – brochure 2000*

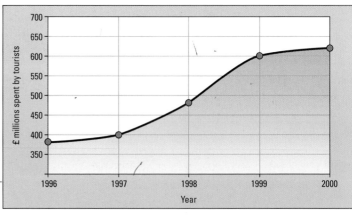

C *Tourism's input into the Norfolk economy 1996–2000*

In a recent survey of visitors to Wroxham, one of the busy villages in the heart of the Broads, some interesting responses were given to the question 'What is your main reason for visiting the Broads?'

Reason	% of respondents	
	Day trippers	Long stay
Scenery/landscape/walking	10	17
Enjoy boating holidays	5	15
Visiting a specific attraction	41	5
Wide range of things to do	22	17
Peace and quiet	3	5
Staying at a holiday centre	0	9
Good accommodation available	0	15
Enjoyed a previous visit	13	8
Other	6	9

D *Visitor survey carried out July 2000*

Q
1 What conclusions can you draw from these figures?

2 Would the responses be different if the survey was carried out in a different location?

3 Does the time of the year that the survey is carried out have an impact on the results?

Tourism – a vital part of the local economy

In addition to the income from tourism as illustrated in **Source C** on page 84, thousands of jobs are linked directly and indirectly to the industry. **Source B** shows how vital the industry is to the economy of three parishes in the heart of the Broads. Wroxham, Hoveton and Horning are all villages that have become dependent on tourism in recent years.

Q
1 What trends do you notice in the period 1951–1991?
2 Discuss how the multiplier effect can lead to further, indirect jobs.
3 If the local economy is so dependent on one industry, are there any worries in the long term?

A *Tourist attractions in the Broads*

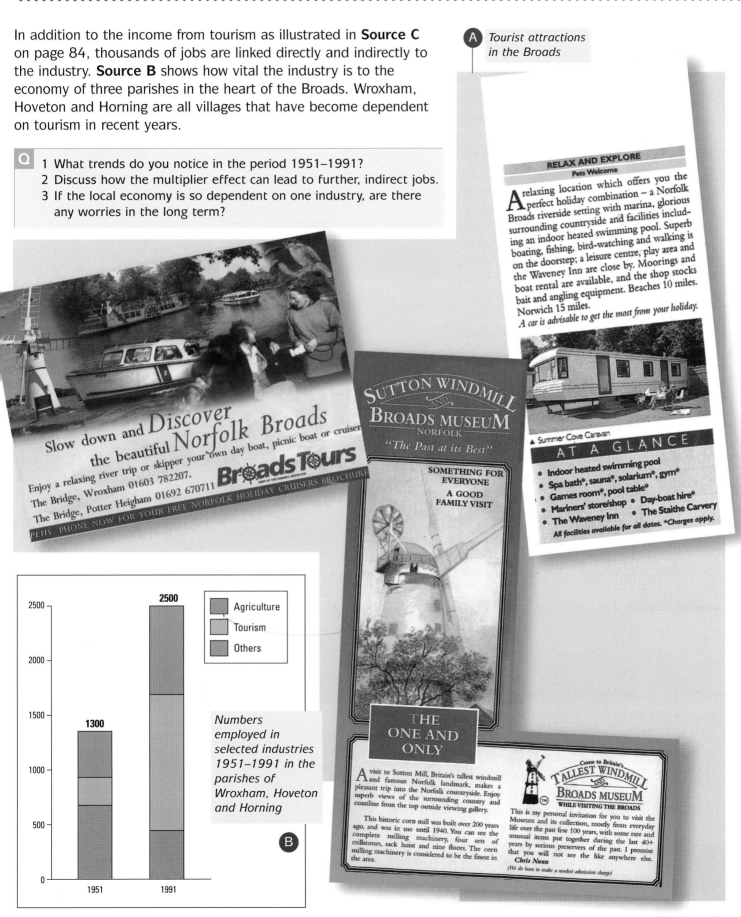

Slow down and Discover the beautiful Norfolk Broads
Enjoy a relaxing river trip or skipper your own day boat, picnic boat or cruiser.
The Bridge, Wroxham 01603 782207. **Broads Tours** PART OF THE TOMKELL GROUP LTD
The Bridge, Potter Heigham 01692 670711
PLUS PHONE NOW FOR YOUR FREE NORFOLK HOLIDAY CRUISERS BROCHURE

RELAX AND EXPLORE
Pets Welcome

A relaxing location which offers you the perfect holiday combination – a Norfolk Broads riverside setting with marina, glorious surrounding countryside and facilities including an indoor heated swimming pool. Superb boating, fishing, bird-watching and walking is on the doorstep; a leisure centre; play area and the Waveney Inn are close by. Moorings and boat rental are available, and the shop stocks bait and angling equipment. Beaches 10 miles. Norwich 15 miles.
A car is advisable to get the most from your holiday.

▲ Summer Cove Caravan

AT A GLANCE
- Indoor heated swimming pool
- Spa bath*, sauna*, solarium*, gym*
- Games room*, pool table*
- Mariners' store/shop • Day-boat hire*
- The Waveney Inn • The Staithe Carvery
All facilities available for all dates. *Charges apply.

SUTTON WINDMILL AND BROADS MUSEUM
NORFOLK
"The Past at its Best"

SOMETHING FOR EVERYONE
A GOOD FAMILY VISIT

THE ONE AND ONLY

A visit to Sutton Mill, Britain's tallest windmill and famous Norfolk landmark, makes a pleasant trip into the Norfolk countryside. Enjoy superb views of the surrounding country and coastline from the top outside viewing gallery.

This historic corn mill was built over 200 years ago, and was in use until 1940. You can see the complete milling machinery, four sets of millstones, sack hoist and nine floors. The corn milling machinery is considered to be the finest in the area.

Come to Britain's **TALLEST WINDMILL AND BROADS MUSEUM**
WHILE VISITING THE BROADS
This is my personal invitation for you to visit the Museum and its collection, mostly from everyday life over the past few 100 years, with some rare and unusual items put together during the last 40+ years by serious preservers of the past. I promise that you will not see the like anywhere else.
Chris Nunn
(We do have to make a modest admission charge)

Numbers employed in selected industries 1951–1991 in the parishes of Wroxham, Hoveton and Horning

B

Bar chart:
- 1951: 1300
- 1991: 2500

Legend:
- Agriculture
- Tourism
- Others

Y-axis: 0, 500, 1000, 1500, 2000, 2500

Economic gain needn't mean environmental pain!

Pressure on the landscape

The built environment

Although tourism is of great importance to the area, it puts tremendous pressure on the landscape and the fragile environment. In the last ten years, increasing awareness and a determined effort by the Broads Authority, who oversee developments in the area, have ensured that any planning proposal is sensitive to the environment. In the boom period 1960–1990, when tourist visits increased from 0.75 million to 2 million, a great deal of damage was done in the interests of accommodating tourists and providing them with a wider range of activities.

Modern accommodation in Horning **B**

In the past, there have been some poor developments that have not been in character with the traditional Broads landscape. They have had a damaging effect on the built environment and spoilt the character of some villages. The planners also allowed too many kiosks, amusement arcades and caravan parks.

With the increase in the number of boats powered by diesel and petrol engines, pollution in the water and bank erosion has had a bad effect on the flora and fauna.

A *Broads businesswoman*

Damage caused by boats

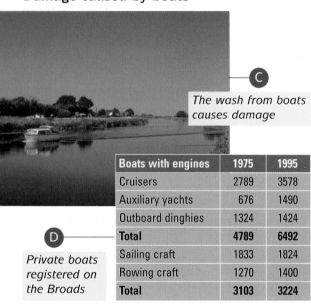
C *The wash from boats causes damage*

D *Private boats registered on the Broads*

Boats with engines	1975	1995
Cruisers	2789	3578
Auxiliary yachts	676	1490
Outboard dinghies	1324	1424
Total	**4789**	**6492**
Sailing craft	1833	1824
Rowing craft	1270	1400
Total	**3103**	**3224**

E *The impact of bank erosion*

Flood wall — Wide rond with reeds and sedge — River bed with rooted plants that absorb energy — High water — Low water

Reed is weakened due to poor water quality — Waves from boat-wash break up reed mats — Erosion below water level caused by boat propeller turbulance — Burrowing animals weaken bank — Dredging can over-steepen bank

Reed rond has been eroded away — Top of piling projects above the water — Sheet steel piling

With an increasing number of boats, especially those with powerful engines, there is a serious problem of bank erosion. **Source E** illustrates how 'natural' river banks can be dramatically changed due, in part, to the wash created by speeding boats. While there are a number of experiments being carried out to reduce the problem, the only easy solution is to create artificial banks using sheet steel piling.

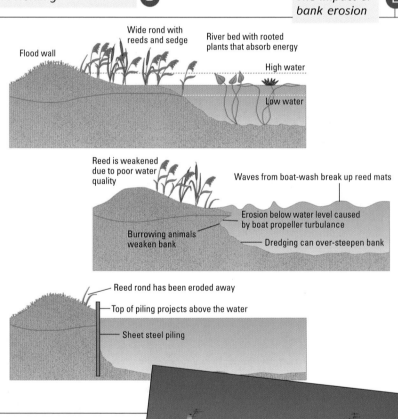
F *Far from a 'natural look' but effective when large numbers of boats are passing.*

Q
1 Why is bank erosion so destructive to wildlife?
2 How easy would it be to control the speed of boats?

Sustainable tourism

One of the prime objectives of the Broads Authority is to promote sustainable tourism. This objective recognises the need to continue to promote tourist activities, in ways that will not harm the environment or the traditions of the area. Conservation of the landscape, wildlife and local traditions should go hand in hand with an increase in the number of visitors. Sources **G**, **H** and **I** suggest ways in which this can be achieved.

An important starting point is to see empty properties refurbished and utilised for tourism. New buildings, built in a traditional style have few problems with planning permission (see **Source K**).

Loved to Death

'Special places need special care, and the Broads like other protected landscapes is in danger of being loved to death by visitors' (from the report of the 1993 National Parks Conference).

The Broads Authority is working with the holiday industry, the Tourist Board and the Countryside Commission to develop the basis for a **sustainable tourist industry.** As well as actively taking steps to improve facilities for tourists which are in keeping with the character of the area, it promotes the Broads as an area of peace and quiet, relaxed boating and enjoyment of the wildlife and the natural beauty of the countryside.

Sustainable tourism aims to ensure the long-term conservation of the Broads. It allows conservation and tourism to benefit each other.

Adapted from publicity material provided by the Broads Authority 1996

G

CANOE THE BROADS

Canoe & kayak hire
Guided trails
Children's Activities
BCU courses
Tel: 01603 737456

NORFOLK SCHOOL OF CANOEING
Randalls Yard, Mill Road, Horstead
http:www.canoeing.co.uk/norfolk

I

The Broads Authority is delighted by enterprises such as this

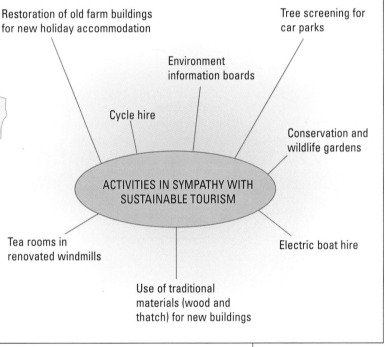

Restoration of old farm buildings for new holiday accommodation

Tree screening for car parks

Environment information boards

Cycle hire

Conservation and wildlife gardens

ACTIVITIES IN SYMPATHY WITH SUSTAINABLE TOURISM

Tea rooms in renovated windmills

Electric boat hire

Use of traditional materials (wood and thatch) for new buildings

H *Options for sustainable tourism*

J *Refurbished old building*

Q 1 Why will the Broads Authority find it difficult to achieve their dual objective of promoting tourism whilst at the same time conserving the landscape, willdlife and local traditions?

2 Compare this case study with the work you did in one of this book (page 13). What are the similarities and the differences?

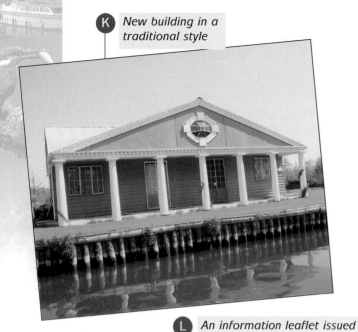

K *New building in a traditional style*

To ensure that any new development is built in sympathy with the environment, the Broads Authority has appointed an 'Enforcement Officer'. Thirty one separate planning proposals were turned down in 1998/9 on the grounds that they did not match the Authority's aim of creating a sustainable future.

fairhaven
WOODLAND & WATER GARDEN

The Fairhaven Woodland and Water Garden comprises 73 hectares (180 acres) of beautiful ancient woodland, water gardens and a private broad, set in the Norfolk countryside at South Walsham. The garden was left in trust by the 2nd Lord Fairhaven in 1973, and was opened to the public in 1975.

M *A good sustainable tourism attraction*

L *An information leaflet issued by the Broads Authority*

Wildlife Water Trail

Get away from it all in a waterborne mystery trail along the dykes, through the reeds and fens of this fascinating reserve. Travel in safety, comfort and tranquility on our Edwardian-style boat, the Electric Eel.

Our experienced guide will show you the wildlife. Marsh harriers, cormorants, swallowtail butterflies, dragonflies, wildflowers and ferns can all be seen at different times of the year. Trips last 50 minutes, including a short walk to the bird hide, and depart from How Hill Staithe (River Ant). Booking is advisable as the boat takes a maximum of eight people. The trip is not suitable for children under 2.

At How Hill, the Broads Authority has built a study centre. This can be hired for conferences.

Surrounding this new facility is a conservation area accessible by many sensitively constructed walkways. In addition, a tour by electric boat is available most of the year.

Sources L and **M** are typical of the kind of enterprise that the Authority is keen to encourage.

Q If the policy of sustainable development is continued, do you think the characteristics of a typical Broads tourist are likely to change?

Activity

1 Search the internet for examples of sustainable tourist projects in Britain and abroad.

2 Use ICT to produce a publicity leaflet for a project near your school, that would be considered both environmentally sound and commercially viable.

Your decision:

Providing for tourism and the environment

The Broads Authority has a commitment to develop areas for public enjoyment while protecting areas of outstanding natural beauty. Developers need to be conscious of these two aims when they submit any planning proposal. In the heart of the Broads, a large area of land has become available for development. A boatyard has vacated an area of land because of the need to expand its construction and sales. Adjacent to this site, a farm has been put up for sale.

Your task

Produce a development plan for the area. Your plan should incorporate a range of ideas to enhance facilities for tourists while, at the same time, recognising the need to be sensitive to the environment.

Source B shows the area with potential for development. **Source C** is a sketch map to show land-use in the surrounding area. Make a larger copy of the sketch map and show your plans for the site. Write a proposal to be submitted to the Broads Authority justifying your ideas.

We are delighted to receive planning applications. Tourists need a place to stay and things to do. We recognise the value of a thriving tourist industry to the local economy. Developers must remember we are determined to protect wildlife and habitats.
Broads Authority officer

This site has huge potential for a range of tourist facilities. I would like to invest a substantial sum in this project, but my bank manager will require a detailed business plan showing how and when I will make a profit.
Local developer

A *Planning carefully to protect the Broads*

B *Potential development area*

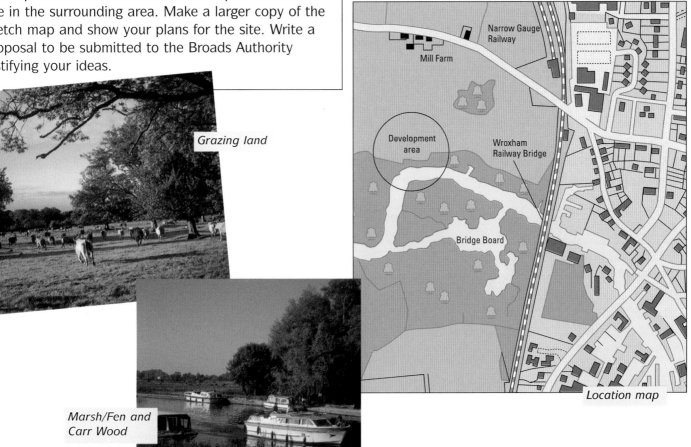

Grazing land

Marsh/Fen and Carr Wood

Location map

89

Hints!

Your sketch map:

- Look at the scale of the map. How far is 100m?
- Use colour shading, symbols, abbreviations and a key to give detail without clutter.
- Look carefully at the existing land-use and access points – the site.
- Use the OS map in Source B to consider the wider picture – the situation.

C *Sketch map to show land-use around the potential development area.*

Coltishall Road

F

F

Mill Farm
(For sale)

F

Bure Valley
Narrow Guage
Railway

I

I

B

Oak
Wood

Wroxham
station

Hints!

Your written justification:

- Justify by recognising how you meet the two aims of the Broads Authority, which will be the organisation considering your proposal.
- What will work in the short term, and what will take longer to achieve?
- Why is zoning important?
- Are you planning for different groups of people?
- Will you face any opposition?
- How will you attempt to overcome opposition?
- Will some aspects of your plan need to be supported by other proposals? Think finance!
- Summarise by talking about an integrated plan.

C

C

A

T

Station Road

Tourist
Information
Office

T

River Bure

Wroxham Bridge Road

T

T

Bridge Broad

Norwich Road

Key

☐ Navigable waterway	**T** Tourism – Hotels, shops, Restaurants	☐ Buildings empty
☐ Land in commercial use	**A** Former boatyard	— Development area
F Farmland	**B** Grazing pasture	N
I Industry	**A** Marsh/fen/Carr Wood	0 100m

Review point

Reflect back on the route through this chapter. In groups of four, prepare a verbal report for your class. Each person should take one question and prepare a brief report summarising the main points that arise. Visual aids to support each aspect of the presentation would help.

- Why is the Broads attractive to tourists?
- How important is this industry to the local economy?
- How can tourism damage the environment?
- What is sustainable tourism? Is it viable?

Activity

Select a similar issue from outside the United Kingdom. Consider the same four questions and prepare a talk based on individual research. You might consider this as part of your wider research into the State of Roraima, Brazil (see Chapter 1).

Glossary

abrasion Erosion caused by material carried by a river or the sea wearing away the land.

adult literacy The percentage of people over 15 years old who can read and write.

agroforestry Farming in which trees are planted together with crops in order to protect the soils.

anticyclone A high pressure system bringing stable, usually dry weather.

attrition Erosion caused when particles transported by a river or the sea are broken up by colliding with one another.

backwash The backward movement of water down the beach after a wave has broken on it.

biodiversity The range of species of plants and animals found in an area.

boulder clay A soft rock deposited by ice sheets, which is easily eroded. Also known as glacial till.

canopy The almost continuous top layer of the rainforest, formed by the crowns of tall trees.

catchment The area of land over which the rain which falls is drained away by a single river and its tributaries.
area

climate The average weather conditions of a place over many years.

coastal Methods of attempting to stop or slow down coastal erosion, such as sea walls, groynes and beach nourishment.
protection

conservation Protection and preservation of ecosystems, environments, animals, plants or man-made objects such as buildings.

conurbation A large urban area formed by the merging together of two or more cities engulfing smaller towns and villages.

cost-benefit The evaluation of the good (benefits) and bad (costs)
analysis effects of a particular action or plan.

counter- The process by which increasing numbers of people
urbanisation move out of urban areas into rural areas.

decomposers The micro-organisms which break down dead organic matter so that the nutrients it contains can be recycled in the ecosystem.

deposition The process of laying down material when water slows down and can no longer carry as much sediment.

depression A low pressure weather system bringing changes in temperature, cloud cover and precipitation as it passes.

development The process by which a country progresses and realises its potential. Levels of development are measured by economic indicators, such as GNP or the progress made from mainly primary to mainly secondary and tertiary activities, or by non-economic indicators such as HDI or the fairness with which wealth is distributed among the population.

development Areas, often suffering industrial decline, which are
areas eligible for economic help through special grants.

development Measurements which can be used to assess the level
indicators of development of a country, such as GNP **or HDI.**

discharge The volume of water flowing in a river per second.

drainage The land area or catchment area drained by a single
basin river and its tributaries.

economic The economic development of a country and the state
well-being of its economy.

ecosystem The links which exist in an area between living things and their environment.

ecotourism Tourism which protects the environment and the way of life of the local people.

El Niño The Spanish name given to an occasional reversal in ocean currents in the Pacific Ocean which affects global weather patterns.

employment The relative numbers of people employed in primary,
structure secondary and tertiary activities.

environment The natural or man-made surroundings where people, plants and animals live.

erosion The process of wearing away the land surface by the movement of agents such as water, ice or wind.

evaporation The process by which water on the Earth's surface is turned into water vapour in the atmosphere.

exploitation Using resources or people to make a profit.

extreme Relatively unusual and/or violent weather events which
weather cause problems ranging from inconveniences to
events disasters.

favela The Brazilian name for a shanty town or squatter settlement where people have built their own houses on land around a city, usually without permission.

food web A representation of the complex feeding links within an ecosystem.

glacial till A soft rock deposited by ice sheets, which is easily eroded. Also known as boulder clay.

global warming	The slowly increasing temperature of the Earth's surface.
greenhouse effect	The build-up of heat caused by molecules of gas in the Earth's atmosphere, notably carbon dioxide, preventing heat from the Earth's surface radiating back into space.
Gross National Product (GNP)	The total value of all the goods and services produced by people and companies from a country in one year. GNP per capita (per person) is the GNP of a country divided by its population.
habitat	The place where a plant or animal lives, and its surroundings, living and non-living.
Human Development Index (HDI)	A measure of social well-being combining measures of life expectancy, educational attainment and income per capita (per person).
hurricane	An intense low pressure system formed in the tropics, bringing strong violent winds and heavy rain. Known as a hurricane in the Caribbean and US, but also known as a typhoon or tropical cyclone.
hydraulic action	Erosion by the force of water dislodging material from a river channel or forcing air into cracks in the rocks causing material to break away.
hydroelectric power (HEP)	Electricity generated by using the energy of falling water.
hydrological cycle	The circulation of water between the sea, the atmosphere and the land.
indigenous people	The first people to settle an area, or those thought to be native to the area.
infant mortality LEDC	(Less Economically Developed Country) These countries are usually defined by having a low GNP per capita. They may also have low scores on other development indicators.
life expectancy	(at birth) The average number of years a person can expect to live.
living standards	The conditions in which people live.
load	The eroded material transported by a river.
longshore drift	The process by which eroded material is transported along the coast, by the action of waves meeting the shore at an angle.
low order services	which are used frequently, and for which people are only prepared to travel short distances, such as newsagents' shops.
MEDC	(More Economically Developed Country) These countries are usually defined by having a high GNP per capita. They may also have high scores on other development indicators.
migration	The movement of people. This can include movements within and between countries.
multinational companies (MNCs)	Large businesses which have operations in more than one country, but usually have their headquarters in an MEDC.
multiplier effect	This occurs when a development, such as a new factory, leads indirectly to other developments, such as new jobs in shops catering for the workers. It can also operate negatively, for instance when a factory closes and other local businesses are affected.
new town	A planned town which has been designed and built for a particular purpose, rather than developing over a period of time.
newly industrialising country (NIC)	A country which has recently changed its economy from mainly agricultural to more industrial and commercial.
plantation	A large farm, often growing only one cash crop and employing a large labour force.
poverty line	A level of income or some other measure, below which people are said to be living in poverty.
precipitation	All forms of moisture reaching the Earth's surface from the atmosphere such as rain, snow, hail, sleet and dew.
primary activities	Activities which extract raw materials from the land or sea, such as mining, quarrying, farming, forestry and fishing.
primary consumer	A herbivore, which eats plants and takes in the energy stored in them.
producers	The plants in an ecosystem, which store the Sun's energy and form the food source for consumer species.
quality of life	How good a person's conditions of life are. It may include the person's level of satisfaction.
receding	The gradual landward progression of a cliff as it is eroded by the sea.
resettlement	The process by which people are moved from their homes in order to settle in another place. They may receive payments or compensation, or sometimes they may be forced to move.
secondary activities	Manufacturing activities which process raw materials into other products, such as chemical or food processing industries.
secondary consumers	Carnivores, which use primary consumers rather than vegetation for their food source.
sediment	The material transported and later deposited by a river.
slumping	The slipping of a large mass of rock down a slope, for instance when part of a clay cliff slips on to the beach after heavy rain.
social costs	The social disadvantages or problems resulting from a particular action.

social well-being The welfare of people, their standard of living and quality of life.

spit A narrow ridge of sand and shingle resulting from longshore drift, attached at one end to the coast.

sprawl The process, often unplanned, by which urban areas spread into their surroundings.

SSSI An area designated as a Site of Special Scientific Interest, often because of its ecosystem.

standard of living The conditions in which people live.

stores The areas of a system in which inputs or outputs remain for a period of time, such as lakes or vegetation in the hydrological cycle.

suburbs Mainly residential areas outside the inner cities in MEDCs.

sustainable A way of using resources to meet the needs of the present, without preventing future generations meeting their own needs.

swash The forward movement of water as a wave breaks on a beach.

tertiary activities Activities which provide services to people and other industries, such as banking or shops.

transfers The processes by which flows occur in a system, such as evaporation or precipitation in the hydrological cycle.

transpiration The process by which plants lose water to the atmosphere.

transportation The movement of material eroded from the land surface to another place, for instance by the sea or by rivers.

undercutting Erosion of the base of a cliff until the rock above collapses.

urban decay The deterioration in the quality of the surroundings which results from a lack of money in the urban economy.

urbanisation The process by which increasing numbers of people live in urban areas rather than in the countryside.

water The exact balance between the water falling in a catchment area as precipitation and the water lost as water vapour or river flow, over a period of time.

water deficit The situation when more water is being lost from a catchment area than is entering it.

water surplus The situation when more water is falling in a catchment area than is being lost from it.

weather Day to day conditions of temperature, precipitation, cloud, sunshine and wind.

weathering The breakdown of surface rocks by the action of the weather, without any movement being involved.

wetland A landscape in which fresh or salt water plays a key role, such as bog, fen, marsh or broads.

wetland A landscape in which fresh or salt water plays a key role, such as bog, fen, marsh or broads.